WHERE HAVE ALL
the Flowers, Fishes,
Birds, Trees, Water,
and Air GONE?

WHERE HAVE ALL

the Flowers, Fishes, Birds, Trees, Water, and Air GONE?

WHAT ECOLOGY IS ALL ABOUT

by

Osborn Segerberg, Jr.

DAVID McKAY COMPANY, INC.
New York

WHERE HAVE ALL THE FLOWERS, FISHES,
BIRDS, TREES, WATER, AND AIR GONE?

Second Printing, May 1971

LIBRARY OF CONGRESS CATALOG CARD NUMBER: 75-142068

MANUFACTURED IN THE UNITED STATES OF AMERICA
VAN REES PRESS • NEW YORK

TO

Mag, Paul, Kate,

and their world

Acknowledgments

I WISH TO THANK Drs. A. Dexter Hinckley, ecologist and entomologist, and Buford Holt, ecologist, at Brookhaven National Laboratory; Gerald Lauer, ecologist and limnologist at New York University's Institute of Environmental Medicine; and Dr. D. M. Vincent Manson, chairman of the Department of Mineralogy, The American Museum of Natural History, for giving generously of their time and knowledge to read and comment on this manuscript. At the same time, I assume complete responsibility for the statements therein.

I thank Drs. Hinckley, Lauer, and Manson as well as Roland Clement, biologist with the National Audubon Society; Dr. Edwin H. Marston, Physics Department, Queens College, City University of New York; and Dr. James Melville, Biology Department, Mercy College, who gave of their personal time to help me in preparation and research for the manuscript.

I give particular thanks to Dr. George M. Woodwell, senior ecologist at Brookhaven National Laboratory, for taking time from his busy schedule to provide guidance and answers to many questions I have asked over 18 months; to Dr. René J. Dubos, professor of environmental biomedicine at The Rockefeller University, for giving unstintingly from his store of wisdom; and to Dr. Charles F. Wurster, Jr., Biology Department, State University of New York at Stony Brook, who has given freely of his expert knowledge of the impact of DDT upon environment. I also wish to express my gratitude to Frank Potter, Executive Director of the Environmental Clearinghouse, Inc., and to Mike Kitzmiller, legislative aide to Congressman Richard Ottinger, for their invaluable assistance to me in the field of environment.

I am indebted to the following scientists for taking the trouble to supply points of information, suggestions, and research papers that helped me with this manuscript: Gordon Barnes, meteorologist with WCBS-TV; Dr. Bernard Berelson, President, The Population Council; Dr. Daniel H. Carson, College of Human Development, Pennsylvania State University; Dr. Preston E. Cloud, Jr., Department of Geology, University of California, Santa Barbara; Dr. Charles F. Cooper, Program Director for Ecosystem Analysis, National Science Foundation; Dr. Paul DeBach, College of Biological and Agricultural Sciences, University of California, Riverside; Dr. Edward S. Deevey, Jr., Biology Department, Dalhousie University; Dr. R. L. Doutt, Acting Dean, College of Agriculture, University of California, Berkeley; Dr. Steven Fretwell, Biology Department, Kansas State University; Dr. H. Bentley Glass, Academic Vice President, State University of New York, Stony Brook; Dr. Carl B. Huffaker, College of Agricultural Sciences, University of California, Berkeley; Dr. Warren Porter, Zoology Department, University of Wisconsin; Robert L. Rabb, Department of Entomology, North Carolina State University; Frederick Sargent, II, M.D., Dean, College of Environmental Sciences, University of Wisconsin-Green Bay; Dr. S. Fred Singer, Deputy Assistant Secretary for Scientific

Programs, U.S. Department of the Interior; Dr. G. Ledyard Stebbins, Division of Genetics, University of California, Davis; Dr. George C. Varley, Department of Entomology, Oxford University.

I am grateful to the following for their permission to use copyrighted material: Oxford University Press to quote from *A Sand County Almanac* by Aldo Leopold, 1966; The M.I.T. Press to use a figure from *Urban Dynamics* by Jay W. Forrester, 1969; *Science* Magazine and Dr. George M. Woodwell to quote from "Radiation and the Patterns of Nature" [G. M. Woodwell, voi. 156 (April 28, 1967), 461–470, copyright 1967 by the American Association for the Advancement of Science] and from "Effects of Pollution on the Structure and Physiology of Ecosystems," [G. M. Woodwell, vol. 168 (April 24, 1970), 429–433, copyright 1970 by the American Association for the Advancement of Science]; *The New York Times* for quotes from an article by George Greenfield on the Dust Bowl (copyright 1937 by The New York Times Company, reprinted by permission); Random House to quote from *How Animals Communicate* by Bil Gilbert (copyright Pantheon Books, a Divison of Random House, 1966); Simon and Schuster, Inc., for permission to quote from *The Worldly Philosophers* by Robert L. Heilbroner, 1953; W. B. Saunders Company to quote from *Fundamentals of Ecology* by Eugene P. Odum, 1959.

Finally, I acknowledge debts of gratitude to Helen Eustis, editor at David McKay Company, Inc., who supplied the inspiration for this book; to Earl Ubell, Science Editor at WCBS-TV News, who suggested that I write it; and to my wife, Nancy, who did all the tedious tasks for this book with unfailing good spirit.

Osborn Segerberg, Jr.
September, 1970

Contents

You will see, too, that modern natural history deals only incidentally with the identity of plants and animals, and only incidentally with their habits and behaviors. It deals principally with their relations to each other, their relation to the soil and water in which they grew, and their relations to the human beings who sing about "my country" but see little or nothing of its inner workings. This science of relationships is called ecology, but what we call it matters nothing. The question is, does the educated citizen know he is only a cog in an ecological mechanism? That if he will work with that mechanism his mental wealth and his material wealth can expand indefinitely? But that if he refuses to work with it, it will ultimately grind him to dust? If education does not teach us these things, then what is education for?

—Aldo Leopold,
A Sand County Almanac

PART ONE

The System

CHAPTER ONE

The Wedding of Ecology and Survival

1

THE ASSIGNMENT would have made James Bond's mouth water. Unfortunately, 007 wouldn't have qualified for the job.

The scenario unfolded in impeccable Ian Fleming fashion. The Center for Short-Lived Phenomena in Cambridge, Massachusetts, received a report from the Southwest Pacific about an unusual concentration of starfish. For the Center, ganglion of an elaborate world communications network, this kind of report is routine. Irruption of Appalachian squirrels or eruption of Costa Rican volcano, suicidal plunge of a meteorite—these kinds of ecological, earth science, or astrophysical reports are filed from various parts of the earth by scientific sentinels. In turn, the Center relays the information to interested parties so that curious scientists can investigate while the phenomenon still is occurring.

When the starfish event came to the attention of the Westinghouse Ocean Research Laboratory at San Diego, California (this was May, 1969), no time was lost in notifying Washington. Discussions were opened with the Office of the Science Adviser to the President, the Department of the Interior, and other Federal officials. By June 6th, a full-scale proposal was submitted to send an ecological expedition to the Pacific. By July 1st, the lead elements of a scientific task force were arriving on the scene.

The array of scientific talent mobilized under a time imperative which suggested wartime emergency was impressive. Five dozen scientists were to examine more than twenty widely separated islands in addition to the Hawaiian group. Merely to list their specializations indicates the spectrum of skills focused on the problem: ichthyology, ecology, and systematics of tropical marine fish, marine geology, biochemistry, genetics, fisheries biology, aquatic environmental management, systematic zoology and zoogeography, coral ecology, coral reef biology, echinoderm ecology and systematics, morphology of echinoderms, invertebrate physiology and ecology, aquaria management, algae, physical oceanography, marine ecology.

The spearhead required considerable logistic support from the U.S. Navy and Coast Guard. Transports, seaplanes, small surface craft, improvised communications and provisions were needed, plus the basic underwater and scientific equipment. A broad-based financial support system had to be arranged. Resources of the Universities of Hawaii and Guam were tapped. The expertise of countless individuals along the way was offered or commandeered. All told, the efforts of many thousands of people went into this remarkable undertaking.

All because of a starfish?

Scientists knew that the starfish *Acanthaster planci* had invaded the Great Barrier Reef off Australia's northern coast a decade earlier. Now the creature appeared to be spreading through the Southwest Pacific. *A. planci* in the past had been an untroublesome citizen of the area—although not completely unobtrusive, for it won the unscientific name "crown-of-thorns."

The crown-of-thorns bristles with an armor of dark

spines over its body and its 12 to 19 arms. The thorns are poisonous and can inflict a painful wound. The adult *A. planci* measures two feet in diameter, with the body accounting for about 6 to 12 inches. The yellow underside consists of scores of tube feet, like living suction cups, and a gastric sac, a retractable stomach that can open and envelop its victim.

What activated the scientists was not so much the crown-of-thorns population explosion or voracious appetite as what it eats. The sea star feeds on the flowerlike little polyps that create and live in coral. The calcareous shell homes are built in colonies upon ancestral structures so that, in time, reefs are constructed. Australia's Great Barrier Reef stretches for 1,250 miles. When crown-of-thorns devour the living polyp, an animal resembling a miniature sea anemone and permanently attached inside its shell, the coral is left a bleached white skeleton. Within days a green algal fuzz covers the dead coral, preventing further colonization. After a while, the reef skeleton tends to break up. Since reefs form protective barriers for the islands or the substructure of atolls, islands themselves are threatened with erosion and, finally, dissolution.

But before that comes to pass the islanders could starve.

If you think of the open ocean as a desert, a sort of mighty liquid Sahara, then coral reefs are the marine oases. Coral reefs are among the most productive natural communities in the world—ranking with estuaries, alluvial croplands, and the intensively farmed patches that agronomists take pride in. Few people are aware of coral reef productivity, of course, since most of the "product" does not pass through human stomachs. Indirectly, nevertheless, the islanders subsist in healthy style on reef marine life. The open ocean could yield perhaps one 35th the food—procured only by much greater labor.

When the coral is killed, the reef community changes. Most of the important food fish disappear, for living coral reef is the foundation for the whole complex structure of reef life. The marine reef community required millions of years to evolve to its present stage of diversity and productivity. It could be the oldest kind of natural community of such complexity on earth. Now it was disappearing in a geologic microsecond. In one night, an adult *A. planci* can graze a coral head that might have taken fifty years to grow. In two and a half years, nearly one-quarter of Guam's reefs was devasted.

Nothing less than the futures of the Micronesian islands of the U.S. Trust Territory were at stake—some won from the Japanese at great cost in American blood—and perhaps the inhabitable islands of the entire Southwest Pacific, as well. One authority, Dr. Porter Kier, chairman of the Paleo-Biology Department of the Smithsonian Institution, said the epidemic could affect marine environments of the whole world.

The ecologists and other scientists were sent to find out: (1) How extensive was the invasion? (2) How much had been so far destroyed? (3) Were controls necessary? (4) Could the infestation be stopped permanently? (5) Why had it happened? A quarter of a century past World War Two, they kept their fingers crossed that it was not another case of too little too late.

The probes ranged across Pacific nameplaces of the war: Guam, the U.S. outpost assaulted and taken by the surging Japanese; Truk, the Japanese bastion pounded by American bombs; Saipan, the nest for B-29s; Tinian, Kwajalein, Palau, the Marshalls, Midway.

It didn't take the scientists long to find the answers to the first two questions. The invasion by *A. planci* was prodigious in scope; the destruction was alarming in rate. The reefs of Tinian were finished, and the coral barriers of three other islands in the Marianas—Guam, Saipan, and Rotat —were scarred and heavily infested. In all, three islands with dead reefs, five endangered, five more (including two atolls in the Marshalls) under siege.

This appraisal gave the answer to the third question about controls. Affirmative. In what must be classed as a desperate effort, the scientific investigation turned into a combat operation: man against Echinodermata Asteroidea Spinulosa Echinasteridae *Acanthaster planci.*

On one side was the panoply of our modern technology. Air transports ferried scientists and support personnel into the Guam staging area. Radiating from this island head-quarters, Navy HU-16 seaplanes skimmed into lagoons, fur-rowing the turquoise waters. In short order, diver-scientists were trolling behind patrol boats, doctors of philosophy formed into four-man killer teams on search-and-destroy missions. Ten fathoms down, in the luminescent waters studded with gaudy tropical fish, was a crown-of-thorns column 10 yards wide, 100 yards long advancing in a weird slow-motion precision on its own search-and-destroy mis-sion, hunting for a reef to eat. In scenes that could be pure science fiction, scuba divers glided down to the starfish phalanx and, moving slowly, zapped each single *A. planci.* One team killed 2,500 starfish in four hours.

While the humans enjoyed mobility, surprise—seeming omnipotence—*A. planci* was a respectable adversary. One of its formidable advantages was decentralization. There was no convenient mastermind for an 007 to remove to provide a simplistic solution or, as it is called in scientific circles, a technological fix. Secondly, there was *A. planci*'s power of regeneration. Stabbing the creature does not nec-essarily ensure its death; slicing it in half may only produce *two* sea stars. Strategically, there was the power of species regeneration; each female is believed capable of laying one million eggs at a time twice a year.

The meaning of these forces can be appreciated when a four-man killer team must deal with what is known as a "front" of crown-of-thorns, a hydra-headed vacuum cleaner advancing over the coral in a herd two miles wide and as deep as a football field. The one effective weapon the humans had—with all our arsenals, our laboratories, and our proving grounds—was a "formalin injector gun." This meant that at about the same time that Neil Armstrong was stepping onto the moon, other Americans were attempting to quell an explosive growth of undersea organisms by injecting *each animal individually* with a formaldehyde syringe.

By sheer diligence, the scientists believed, they brought the invasion of Guam under control. But Dr. Richard Chesher, leader of the operation, reported that it was merely "a temporary control to decrease the rate of coral destruction until studies in more detail are complete and long-term biological controls are established." The answer to question four (Can the invasion of crown-of-thorns be blocked permanently?) could depend upon the answer to question five: Why did *Acanthaster planci*, a starfish which has been a relatively rare creature for centuries, perhaps millennia, perhaps always—why did its population suddenly explode?

The scientists reasoned that the sudden expansion of the crown-of-thorns population could be the result of either a change in the animal or a change in its environment. If a change in the animal, biologists or echinoderm specialists would have enormous trouble tracking it down. Not even a minute fraction of one percent of the species on earth have been studied in the detail necessary to provide that kind of answer. Fortunately, it seemed the less likely of the two categories. If a change in environment, it could either be physical in nature—the appearance of favorable oceanographic conditions—or biological.

Dr. Chesher and his colleagues favored the latter (changed ecological relationships) as the most likely explantation. The adult *A. planci* has one known predator in the area—a large mollusc, *Charonia tritonis*, called triton. Tritons are encased in shells highly prized by shell collectors. One Australian authority calculates that collectors took at least a hundred thousand tritons from Great Barrier Reef in the decade before 1960 when the starfish assault got underway there. Three hundred miles of that 1,250-mile reef are under attack by the starfish. On the islands the incentive to hunt the conches also is strong: a single triton shell brings more profit to the finder than any other natural product of the reef.

Still, the scientists found *A. planci* infestations in reefs where triton hunting is not practiced and absence or low numbers of the starfish in other places where collection of the conches is heavy.

Another hypothesis suggested that rising levels of DDT and other organo-chlorines may have interfered with the reproductive success of tritons and in that way reduced their population.

But a more likely stage for the limitation of the starfish population is when they are larvae—immobile and defenseless. Ironically, crown-of-thorns eggs are consumed by the very coral polyps fed upon by the adult starfish. Since World War Two, blasting and dredging have become frequent activities on the Pacific islands. Dynamite explosions break and overturn coral—providing a bare and safe surface for starfish larvae to settle upon and develop. This might have been the method by which so many crown-of-thorns got a chance to grow into adults.

There was still another theory—that DDT (again) and the other long-lived chlorinated hydrocarbons have interfered with planktonic microorganisms that also feed on the starfish larvae.

Dr. Chesher's report concludes: "The existing evidence implies that the infestations are induced by human activities; collection of tritons, local destruction of reefs, and pollution offer plausible explanations of the outbreaks. Possibly all are simplifications. There may be other causes yet to be considered."

The *Acanthaster planci* starfish is clearly doing something it has not done for a long time (there would be evidence of an outburst of such magnitude during the past several centuries), if ever—something it shouldn't be doing. This judgment does not apply to the individual *A. planci*, which obviously is only doing its thing, which happens to be eating coral polyps. But if *A. planci*, the species, continues this way, it will destroy its own habitat, upon which a good number of other populations depend as well. A curb to the plague already has been observed. When the starfish consume all available live coral reef in one location and can find no new forage, the herd apparently dies. So the infestation surely will come to an end. The scientists simply are trying to bring about control before crown-of-thorns can devastate a biologically important part of the Southwest Pacific Ocean.

That is what can happen when one seemingly unimportant species escapes its ecological bonds.

Who is at fault? Is *A. planci* the villain, or a pawn? Should we blame shell collectors? Excoriate the manufacturers of DDT? How about those well-meaning administrators who said blast and dredge for progress? Or the engineers who served them? While no scientist alludes to the bombs of World War Two, Dr. Chesher's report notes that the first sightings of abnormal starfish concentrations date to that conflict. (Truk, for instance, is one of the seriously infested islands.) Even if a responsible commander could have known there may have been a risk, would he have given it a second thought? Such a consideration would have been preposterous.

Instead of trying to assign blame, ecology poses another question: with nearly one and a half million known species of plants and animals, with virtually all species possessing the potential for explosive growth, with the human species technologically powerful while ecologically ignorant— *where will it happen next?*

2

The Soviet Union has its Tupolev, France its Concorde, the United States its SST. These airplanes are meant (A) to carry passengers great distances very quickly and (B) to make money for their respective manufacturers and nations from the commercial air transport industry. In order to accomplish (A) and (B), the aircraft must (C) fly through the stratosphere. Unlike the troposphere, which extends up to about 40,000 feet and where all the pollution is swept around and to some extent dissipated, the stratosphere is extremely stable. Fine, light combustion products from those aircraft would remain in the stratosphere for long periods of time, and accumulate. Meteorologist Vincent Schaefer estimates that no more than a thousand airplanes regularly criss-crossing the stratosphere within a few years will produce an intolerable pollution. Of course, that's just an educated warning.

But as it happens, nature has given us previews of what can occur. Ecologist Kenneth E. F. Watt reports that, based on nearly a century of records kept in England and Wales, there were two great peaks of influenza—the world pandemic of 1918 which took 30 million lives and another in 1889. The 1918 epidemic followed by six years the volcanic eruption of Katmai in Alaska; the earlier epidemic took place six years after that of Krakatoa. Katmai and Krakatoa blasted into the stratosphere volcanic matter that spread a cover of fine particles around the earth—Europeans remarked at the time the spectacular sunsets filtered through Krakatoa's shroud. Studies have shown that what also happened after these major volcanic eruptions was that annual temperatures, particularly in winter, were abnormally low for five years and remained somewhat depressed for five additional years. What amounted to a changed climate could have altered the relationships in the human-influenza virus system.

Dr. Watt found a second biological correlation to the volcanic eruptions. The Hudson Bay Company in Canada kept records from 1821 to 1934 on the taking of lynx furs. These unique records have served many ecologists making long-range population studies, and have been particularly useful in examining predator-prey relationships. The lynx is a predator of the snowshoe hare and the records show a cyclic oscillation of the two populations. As hares grew more plentiful so did lynxes, until the abundant felines killed off great numbers of hares. The following year, with few hares to feed on, the lynx population also crashed. A nadir in the lynx population occurred about every ten years, indicated by the few pelts recorded by the Hudson Bay Company.

Dr. Watt found exceptionally low lynx nadirs in the years 1889 and 1918—that same six-year time lag after the volcanic eruptions. He had to go all the way back to 1842 for a comparable low—and that year happens to be seven years after the great volcanic eruption of Coseguina in Nicaragua in 1835.

Dr. Watt documented still a third correspondence to the Katmai and Krakatoa eruptions for an insect, a pine looper in Germany.

A quite independent line of research has established that there was a tremendous volcanic eruption on Santorini, an island southwest of Greece and north of Crete in the eastern Mediterranean, at about 1400 B.C. There are indications that this convulsion surpassed mighty Krakatoa. Even if Santorini were only of equal magnitude to Krakatoa, the roar of the explosions would have been heard as far away as Gibraltar, Scandinavia, and Central Africa. The ash and gas cast into the atmosphere caused total darkness in the eastern Mediterranean with long-lasting meteorological effects.

The cataclysm with its attendant tidal waves and earthquakes, it now seems evident, ended the Minoan civilization and drove survivors from their Aegean Islands to the mainland to settle what in two centuries would become Homer's Greece. But of most pertinence here, the prevailing winds at the time of the Santorini eruption were believed northwesterly, blowing the pollution over the skies of Egypt. Dragoslav Ninkovich and Bruce Heezen of Columbia University's Lamont Geological Observatory have quoted from ancient Egyptian papyrus which undoubtedly referred to this particular event: "We know not what has happened throughout the land . . . It is confusion that thou bringest throughout the land together with the noise of tumult . . . O that the earth would cease from noise . . . The towns are destroyed . . . Upper Egypt has become wasted . . . Blood is everywhere . . . Plague is throughout the land."

Drs. Ninkovich and Heezen go on to say, "The similarity between the events described in the Egyptian scriptures

(Griffith, 1890; Gardiner, 1909, 1914) and the plague described in the Old Testament has been pointed out by many historians. Breasted (1951) concluded: 'Specimens of this remarkable class of Egyptian literature may be traced as late as the early Christian centuries, and we cannot resist the conclusion that it furnished the Hebrew prophets with the form and to a surprising extent also with the content of Messianic prophecy.' Bennett (1963) was the first to suggest that the Egyptian plagues may have been an aftermath of the Minoan eruption of Santorini. Galanopoulis (1964) reached the same conclusion . . ."

On this evidence, then, it appears that the alteration of climate or atmosphere beyond some undetermined point will produce profound effects upon biological systems.

We don't know.

"So much of the danger to man," said ecologist LaMont Cole, "is summed up in that simple phrase, 'We don't know.' " Dr. Cole's remark was contained in a speech to the American Association for the Advancement of Science in December, 1967. The address "Can the World Be Saved?" was one of the early ecological pronouncements questioning the fate of the human species. It was decidedly a minority report.

Two years later, President Nixon signed into law the National Environmental Policy Act of 1969. Two months after that, environmental crusader Barry Commoner was featured on the cover of *Time*. The caption read: "Ecologist Barry Commoner, The Emerging Science of Survival." Two months after that, the United States marked "Earth Day." And a few months after that, the President proposed setting up an Environmental Protection Agency, concentrating in it environmental powers once held by a number of Cabinet departments in a drastic revision of the executive branch.

Even in an era of instant communications and a nation of fickle passions, the transition from Cole to *Time* was remarkable. One year ecologists were unknown, unwanted, and unheeded, the next they were hurrahed as mankind's last best hope. One wag quipped that people would grow tired of ecology before they knew what the word meant.

3

Ecology stems from the Greek word *oikos*, meaning house or place to live. Literally, ecology is the study of organisms in their homes. An original meaning of economy, which derives from the same Greek base, was management of household affairs. The social science of economics is concerned with the production, distribution, and consumption of goods and services. The science of ecology is concerned with the production, distribution, and consumption of energy in natural systems. The intertwining of the two concepts can be seen in a definition proposed by the German biologist Ernst Haeckel, who is generally credited with first using the term ecology in 1866: "By ecology we mean the body of knowledge concerning the economy of nature— the investigation of the total relations of the animal to its inorganic and to its organic environment."

And that is close to the generally accepted definition for ecology today: the science of the interrelations of organisms with their environment and other organisms.

But there are other definitions:

A pioneering English ecologist, Charles Elton, wrote in 1927, "Ecology is a new name for a very old subject. It simply means scientific natural history."

A more modern way of looking at it, according to Professor Eugene P. Odum of the University of Georgia, is "the study of the structure and function of nature."

A panel on ecology for a National Academy of Sciences survey of the life sciences said that ecology's domain could be considered to be environmental biology. But the panel found this was not a completely satisfying definition, for ecologists are concerned with significant interactions of complex living systems. "Ecologists," the panel said, "are trained to focus on the interfaces between systems—on problems that fall between the cracks of 'basic' sciences."

Frank Fraser Darling said ecology could be called "a science of identifying causes and consequences."

Paul Sears offered, "Ecology—A Subversive Subject."

Plainly, the science of ecology is neither simple nor simplistic, but it is not hard for anyone to grasp its truths once they are postulated. The multiple definitions suggest the strength as well as weakness of ecology. From the start it enjoyed immense freedom of investigation, but up to very recent years suffered from a diffuseness stemming from a multiplicity of beginnings, in natural history, evolution, genetics, husbandry, plant geography, and physiology, as well as from the very magnitude of its objective. Ecology aimed at becoming an exact natural science of nothing less, as it turned out, than all the living relationships of existence. While this catholicity would attract a broad range of curious intellects, it could also generate parochial scorn. After all, how thin can you spread expertise? On top of that, it was "different" from orthodox sciences.

Ecology suffered an identity or "image" crisis at its start of operations. For most of this century ecologists were scientific pariahs. Dr. Darling told a meeting of scientists in 1963, "It was academic suicide to be an ecologist except incidentally to an acknowledged position in botany or zoology."

In order to understand how ecologists survived "under cover," it is necessary to visualize ecology's relationship to other sciences. Speaking of an ecologist, Dr. Sears wrote, "When he enters a forest or a meadow he sees not merely what is there, but what is happening there." Ecology is a science of process, and as such is entwined with many sciences, particularly the biological sciences. Ecology began as a branch of biology.

As knowledge grew, biology, the umbrella science of life, split into more manageable divisions. Botany and zoology were natural enough, since those separate studies of plants and animals had long existed. Zoology subdivided, for instance, into mammalogy, the study of mammals; ornithology, the study of birds; entomology, the study of insects; or protozoology, the study of one-celled animals. But the continuum of reality forced biologists to recognize the relation of their studies with other major domains of science. The acknowledgment of the convergence of biological and chemical processes is the science of biochemistry.

Ecology plays a role in all these sciences. The biochemist who wants to find out how a substance like DDT behaves in a food chain must employ ecological knowledge and principles. A marine biologist is a scientist who studies ocean life. If he specializes in bottom life, the relationships of organisms who live in the substrate, he also would be a benthic ecologist. A limnologist, a scientist who studies lakes and still waters, also could be a benthic ecologist.

Today, ecology can stand as an independent science, although virtually no undergraduate school gives a degree in it, and the Compleat Ecologist is a rare (though hardly endangered) species. While there may be 4,000 practicing ecologists in the United States, only about two dozen of them are qualified or daring enough to undertake large ecosystem investigations. And very few are busy with innovative theory.

The multi-disciplinary mastery implied is awesome. For example, while "nature" is the ostensible subject, cornerstones of the science are the physical laws of thermodynamics and the biogeochemical cycle—bio for biological, geo for geological. A knowledge of advanced mathematics is recommended if you want to be creative, and conversance with the computer is necessary for population models and ecosystem simulation. Radioactive tracers and remote sensing have become useful tools in ecology's search for information. In the latter technique, an airplane with ten different cameras might take pictures in infrared, in, say, ten different wavelengths of a grassland under study. Then computers scan the photos for an instant assessment of a large area.

In addition to utilizing the newest technology, ecology feeds on the latest information developed by other sciences.

4

Yet with all this modernity, the taproots of ecology reach into antiquity. It gives one an uncanny feeling to go back more than twenty-three centuries to find that the central thesis of Plato's *Republic* is a cardinal law of today's science of ecology.

In the *Republic*, Plato has his spokesman, Socrates, lead a group of men on a long, tortuous quest of the mind to discover what justice is. In addition to our understanding of the word today, justice to the ancient Greeks also contained some of the qualities of virtue, rectitude, and the good life.

Wielding questions like a sculptor's chisel, the narrator cuts away all the definitions advanced by the others until only his own remains. Justice, says Plato, is "that one man should practice one thing only, the thing to which his nature was best adapted." Justice is "the having and doing what is a man's own." In Plato's ideal society everyone did his own work—the work for which he was best suited—to produce the most effective harmonious whole.

Ecology has learned that this is exactly what takes place *in nature*. The plant or animal most qualified to carry out a particular function in the system occupies that niche, or job category, as we might call it.

If ecology as a way of looking at things goes back to Plato, its structure is traced to Plato's student Aristotle. Whereas Plato was a theoretician, Aristotle was an empiricist. In zoological gardens stocked from the expanding empire of a former pupil, Alexander the Great, Aristotle conducted extensive studies of nature. From these observations, he divined an order in the profligate variety of life. "Nature makes so gradual a transition from the inanimate kingdom that the boundary lines which separate them are indistinct and doubtful," he wrote, more than two millennia before the isolation of the virus. As he categorized an ascending order of animals, he reasoned that structures of life increase in complexity with a corresponding growth in intelligence and that the goal is mastery of environment.

While Aristotle was known to a succession of scholars and ecclesiastics through the centuries as "The Philosopher," he acquired in modern times another title, "Father of Biology."

A successor to Aristotle, Theophrastus, advanced the study of plants, and his consideration of plant associations and their relation to environment actually anticipated the ecological mode.

Those first brilliant gleams of discovery in natural science in the West were not to be equaled until after civilization awakened from its long medieval torpor. Beginning in the 15th century, men once again turned to nature for information and instruction. The first important result in biology came in 1543 with Vesalius's revelations of human anatomy. It took nearly another century before William Harvey mapped the circulation of blood.

By the 1700s the collections of animals and plants gathered during the great explorations were piling up in cluttered confusion. It became obvious that the prodigality of life had hopelessly overwhelmed the system of classification that had persisted virtually unimproved for 2,000 years since Aristotle. The situation was rescued from chaos by a Swedish naturalist with a passion for codifying, Carl von Linné. Along with everything else, he gave himself a Latin name, Carolus Linnaeus.

He found that nature so loved profusion that, after dividing plants and animals into separate kingdoms, Linnaeus still was forced to ramify through six more major subdivisions in his new catalogue of life. The animal divisions are: Kingdom, Phylum, Class, Order, Family, Genus, Species. In the case of man, the classifications are: Animal Chordata Mammalia Primata Hominidae *Homo sapiens*. Generally, the last two names in the "dead" and immutable Latin are the ones used in scientific papers to identify a particular organism. After Linnaeus, natural scientists could communicate in a common language.

It was not until the beginning of the 19th century that biology, the formal science we know today, began to take form. But, significantly, it was a political economist of that time who exerted the important long-range effect upon the future ecology. In 1798 the Reverend Thomas Malthus published his famous *Essay on the Principles of Population* as an antidote to utopian views of society. In the essay, Malthus noted that plants and animals have the potential to expand to "fill millions of worlds in the course of a few thousand years," but lack of space and nourishment prevents this from happening. The formula came to be known as population tends to increase geometrically while food production tends to increase arithmetically. This great law of necessity rules, Malthus said, "And the race of man cannot by any efforts of reason, escape from it. Among plants and animals its effects are waste of seed, sickness, and premature death. Among mankind, misery and vice."

Charles Darwin read that essay forty years later. Darwin had been to the Galapagos Islands, had returned from the voyage of the *Beagle*, and was pondering the theory of evolution. He had observed how species change in time (comparing fossils with living representatives) and space (members living on the isolated Galapagos with counterparts on the mainland). He concluded that the changes he observed were the result of evolution. After reading Malthus, Darwin conceived how evolution worked. "Now, can it be doubted," he wrote, "from the struggle each individual has to obtain subsistence, that any minute variation in structure habits, or instincts adapting that individual better to new conditions would tell upon its vigor and health? In the struggle it would have a better *chance* of surviving; and those of its offspring which inherited the variation, be it ever so slight, would also have a better *chance*."

The promulgation of evolution through natural selection in 1859—the last great biological theory derived solely from observation, without experimentation—had the curious effect of driving zoologists indoors. In order to verify or disprove the theory of evolution, half of the zoolgists moved into museums to study fossils while the remainder retired to laboratories to peruse the structure and function of animals. Botanists applied themselves as assiduously to their kingdom. Everyone discovered that the work of Linnaeus badly needed repair, so considerable scientific effort once again was devoted to classifying, the science of taxonomy.

Thus there was a hiatus between the 1860s, when ecology was born out of the ferment of Darwin's perceptions ("web of life," the phrase which probably best describes the subject, is Darwin's), and the turn of the 20th century when it took its first steps. It is pertinent to remember that the more developed sciences of the time were moving rapidly: the microbiology of Pasteur and Koch was producing a medical revolution, in physics Einstein was preparing to unlock the atom and restructure the universe. "Scientific ecology was first started," Charles Elton writes, "by botanists, who finished their classification sooner than the zoologists, because there are fewer species of plants than animals, and because plants do not rush away when you try to collect them."

Ecology's first great accomplishment resulted from studies made at the Lake Michigan sand dunes near Gary, the same dunes that became a conservation *cause célèbre* in the second half of this century. Henry Cowles, followed later by Victor Shelford and Frederic Clements, contributed to the intriguing discovery that there is a definite, predictable sequence of plant communities from bare ground or lowly weed patch to mighty forest.

By 1927, Charles Elton's *Animal Ecology* diagrammed the dynamics and structure of the animal community and viewed animal and plant populations as an integrated whole. "There are numerous gases, liquids, and solids circulating everywhere in nature," Elton wrote, "the study of which is carried on by physicists, chemists, meteorologists, astronomers, etc.; certain parts of these great systems are, as it were, cut off and formed into little temporary systems which are animals and plants." Elton lamented that zoologists had been studying dead animals so long in museums and laboratories that they had overlooked the important fact that live animals are part of their environment.

There were other growing pains for the young science. The multi-disciplinary nature of ecology put strains on scientists who by training and tradition tended to become specialists. A cracking good botanist understandably might be just an average zoologist. The lack of expertise in certain areas led to errors and may have delayed ecology's development. Nevertheless, the necessity for scientists to venture into many fields despite the risks to pride, the inception of a multi-discipline science, was to become ecology's great strength for future tasks.

In 1935, Arthur Tansley, an Englishman like Elton, defined the concept of an ecosystem, putting the living animal and plant community together with the non-living environment. Using Tansley's concept and incorporating work in bioenergetics by August Thienemann in Germany, a young American, Raymond Lindeman, fused the dynamics of an ecosystem into a framework accessible to abstract analysis. With the publication of his paper, "The Trophic-Dynamic Aspect of Ecology," in 1942, and studies by G. Evelyn Hutchinson on the biogeochemical cycle, the science gained its basic working unit—the ecosystem. With this Rosetta Stone, ecologists could begin to decipher nature's hieroglyphics. Lindeman died before his paper was published, at the age of 27.

From blurred beginnings in several 19th-century disciplines, the diverse insights of ecology began to come into powerful focus. From humble beginnings with plants to the expanded knowledge of plant-animal communities, now the scope of ecology opened to study a whole unit of landscape —a pond, a meadow, a watershed, a forest.

The true worth of the ecosystem concept was not fully appreciated and accepted until the middle 1950s. And it was not until 1962 that the use of computers and modern systems analysis made the theoretical knowledge manageable.

In every discipline, a unit for measuring is essential. In nutrition, it's the calorie; in acoustics, the decibel; in geography, the square mile; in astronomy, the light year. For ecology, the science concerned with interrelationships and processes, it became the naturally inclusive unit or ecosystem. When one considers the incredible number of species (not to mention individuals) in even a modest ecosystem —so many, in fact, that a complete inventory has never been made—then one begins to value the need for a computer to handle the mass of data entailed. Furthermore, a computer simulation—simpler than, but approximating the natural ecosystem—can be set up for a systems analysis similar to studies made for corporations. Instead of asking what happens to the company if it markets product X, ecologists might ask what happens to the other species if all the rabbits are removed or what happens to the ecosystem if it is sprayed with 2,4-D.

Ecologists quietly proceeded to accumulate a fascinating body of information and statistics. But as they ventured farther into nature's realm, they advanced deeper into paradox: the more they learned, the more they realized how much more there was to know. Actually, while it came about in gradual, undramatic, unheralded fashion, revealing the miracle of the commonplace may have been ecology's finest achievement. "The outstanding scientific discovery of the twentieth century," wrote the philosophic founder of wildlife game management, Aldo Leopold, before his death in 1948, "is not television, or radio, but the complexity of the land organism."

If ecology was making a significant contribution to man's knowledge of his world, the information was well screened from the public. By the standards of news editors, the bird watcher existed only as an antic irrelevancy, and the plant watcher went unnoted. There were occasional "nature" books which tended to exclaim at "the wonder of it all." But ecologists dissociated themselves from emotionalism. They considered themselves professionals, in contrast to naturalists and conservationists whom they looked upon as amateurs.

This attitude posed something of a dilemma, since ecologists were intimately involved with nature and the logic of their studies led them to believe in the utter necessity of conservation as a way of surviving. But ecologists were scientists, not do-gooders. Definitely not espousers of causes. Retiring men, really. And for all its good intentions, the conservation movement after the Second World War was a reed holding back a national flood of exploitation.

The publication of Rachel Carson's *Silent Spring* in 1962 sounded the tocsin for change. Because that revolutionary book lacked some of the scientific data (facts that did not exist because of the dereliction of responsible governmental and scientific authorities) to make an airtight indictment, scientists who should have known better ducked the ensuing public controversy. Subsequent verifying information proved how very right Miss Carson had been in her general estimate of the pesticide menace.

In 1965, a committee of the Ecological Society of America declared, "Rachel Carson's book *Silent Spring* created a tide of opinion which will never again allow professional ecologists to remain comfortably aloof from public responsibility. The importance of this book and its effect on public opinion, national scientific policy, and the status of professional societies with respect to public affairs can hardly be overstated."

Long before *Silent Spring*, ecologists had cause to appreciate the disturbance of natural systems by man. The land organism was complex enough, but ecologists also encountered complicating distortions of human origin. Ecologists resented this intrusion into their laboratory (and thus became sympathetic to conservationists' goals). In order to find out what is normal, it was necessary to study pristine nature. But that was becoming as rare as the Bengal tiger. Man-made distortion turned all ecology research into a race against time. But the environment couldn't wait for the ecologists to finish their education. In what might be described as a shotgun wedding, ecologists began studying, deliberately investigating, what man was doing to his habitat.

Until that moment, ecology and ecologists had performed in almost perfect social anonymity. Now they were entering history's mainstream, a handful of observers, trained by an unorthodox science to look at reality in a different way from their fellow men.

Where physicists calibrated the power of nuclear bombs, ecologists traced unleashed radionuclides. Where engineers constructed efficient energy plants, ecologists calculated the thermal waste. Where chemists conjured plastics, ecologists detected venomous polychlorinated biphenyls in food chains. Where agriculturists championed DDT, ecologists contemplated the toxic permeation of the world's biological systems. Where the military sprayed herbicides to save lives, ecologists saw the massacre of ecosystems. Where the World Health Organization defeated malaria and organ transplanters inspired fantasies of personal immortality, ecologists stared at the human population curve. Where "realists" weighed the balance of trade, ecologists monitored the balance of oxygen, carbon dioxide, nitrogen, and phosphorous. Where economists prescribed magnification of GNP, ecologists charted the frontiers of environmental bankruptcy.

If man, like *Acanthaster planci*, is caught in an inexorable process of destroying his habitat, how can he stop himself?

In answer to such a question ecologist David Gates said, "All we're struggling for at the moment is that we understand, fundamentally, these ecological issues. If we understand, it doesn't necessarily mean we will survive; it doesn't necessarily mean we will solve the problems, but it does mean we stand a fighting chance. Without it we don't."

In order to share ecologist Gates' perspectives and evaluate his judgment, it is necessary to look at classical ecology —if such a term can be applied to such a young science. The validity of the ecological indictment is based upon what the science has learned from biological systems.

CHAPTER TWO

The Closed System

1

"It was now a case of survival," said Captain James A. Lovell, Jr. He was describing for the members of the Senate Aeronautical and Space Sciences Committee the situation of Apollo 13 after an explosion cut off most of the electrical power and with it their other supplies aboard the moon-bound spacecraft he shared with astronauts Jack Swigert and Fred Haise, Jr. Using their lunar module *Aquarius* as a liferaft, the three astronauts in conjunction with Houston Mission Control met the crisis with a series of improvisations that testify to human resourcefulness. With skill and nerve, Lovell fired the engine of *Aquarius* to maneuver the spaceship into a "slingshot" course around the moon and back home to earth.

With that correction, the astronauts' return to earth was assured by the laws of physics. Now their survival depended upon the rules of biology. Their story serves as an excellent illustration of the closed system.

While mankind waited and prayed, Lovell, Swigert, and Haise concentrated on "consumables." The most immediately vital of them was oxygen. The three astronauts required about one pound of the vital life-giving element every three hours. After initial calculations, Lovell discov-

ered to his relief that there was sufficient oxygen for them to
make it back. But water was in critically short supply and,
in fact, the astronauts consumed the last of their drinking
water during their final day in space. Water still remained
in the environmental control system, but that was needed
for coolant. Now, while the human organism may live without water for about a week under ideal conditions (the
survival span would be cut to a fraction of that time in a
desert or jungle) the body's effective functioning quickly
becomes impaired by water deprivation. What is commonly
known as dehydration causes a deteriorating chemical imbalance in the body; no one can predict for sure its consequences upon the urinary tract, in which Haise, in fact, did
develop an infection.

Because of the absolute necessity to conserve electrical
power, all equipment and systems outside *Aquarius* were
turned off and the temperature gradually dropped to 38 degrees in the darkened, roomier *Odyssey* command module
that for a while served as a bedroom. The three voyagers
huddled in the cramped lunar module where the temperature was 50 degrees. Lovell and Haise considered putting
on the heavy space suits they would have worn on the
moon, but discarded the notion for fear the suits would
cause excessive perspiration that in the cold module could
lead to pneumonia. Fortunately, the temperature stayed at a
tolerable level.

Another and perhaps the most serious problem soon
became apparent. While there was enough oxygen to
breathe in, the environmental system of the small lunar
module *Aquarius* was inadequate to take care of what the
men breathed *out*, carbon dioxide. In our natural atmosphere, carbon dioxide forms only about .03 percent—three
parts in 10,000—of the total air. In normal operations
aboard the spacecraft, the CO_2 content is allowed to reach

33 times that amount, becoming one percent of the astronauts' atmosphere. But if the carbon dioxide climbs to two percent, an astronaut's performance will begin to deteriorate after eight hours. If the spacemen continued to reuse air with ever higher amounts of CO_2, they would grow uncomfortable, then drowsy, and finally drop off to sleep, permanently.

The carbon dioxide is removed by filtering the air through canisters of lithium hydroxide, a compound that can absorb great amounts of carbon dioxide. *Aquarius* simply did not have enough lithium hydroxide to cleanse the waste air of three men for an extended length of time, but the command module *Odyssey* had two big canisters. With careful instructions from Houston Control, the astronauts rigged a makeshift pipeline from spacesuit hoses, friction tape, and cardboard to siphon the air through the lithium hydroxide in *Odyssey*. And so the air was scrubbed of the potentially lethal CO_2.

Finally, there was the problem of urine. Normally, Apollo travellers dump their urine through a vent in the command module, but because of the precariousness of their navigational situation they were reluctant to risk the slightest disturbance to their trajectory attitude. Every bag in the lunar module was used to store the waste from three bodies.

These were the survival factors met successfully on a space voyage that, after the accident, took 80 hours.

National Aeronautics and Space Administration scientists have been studying life survival for such projected voyages as the Mars Stopover—400 days—or the Jupiter Flyby —1400 days. The difference in life-support systems between the one used for Apollo and that needed for Mars or Jupiter is one of kind, not degree. In the voluminous NASA publication *Parametric Study of Manned Life Support Systems*, the apparatus used on Apollo is known as an Open System. The life-giving essentials are brought on board the spaceship, consumed en route and the waste eliminated. It is a one-way system with a fixed limit to consumption and survival. In order to reach Mars, since no spacecraft is big enough to carry all the consumables for a one-way system, a closed system is required.

In an exploratory conference on the Closed Life-Support System held at Ames Research Center, Moffet Field, California, in April, 1966, NASA's Assistant Director for Life Sciences, Harold Klein, noted, "Scientists and engineers have been concerned for many years with the challenging problems inherent in the fabrication of a closed life-support system. Aside from the prospects of difficult engineering hurdles yet to be overcome, it is also clear that enormous gaps exist in our fundamental knowledge about many aspects of this problem. For example, it is impossible at this time even to summarize man's nutritional requirements completely. Virtually nothing is known about human production of contaminants and not much more is available regarding man's tolerance levels to such materials. Biological agents that might be employed to convert human wastes to useful foodstuffs or fuels are themselves incompletely studied particularly from the point of view of their usefulness as potential 'chemosynthesizers.' On the other hand, physiochemical procedures to accomplish these end results have barely been initiated."

Since that conference, NASA scientists have been working on 44 possible life-support subsystems or parts of subsystems that permit 675,000 kinds of combinations. It is interesting to note that the lithium hydroxide removal of carbon dioxide aboard Apollo was one of the few already functional components of the recycling circuits under test for a closed support system.

Most likely methods of converting human metabolic wastes into food, water, and oxygen—thus closing the essential loop—appear to be through the physicochemical synthesis of sugar-like substances such as glycerol from carbon dioxide and water and the biochemical growth of edible *Hydrogenomonas eutropha* bacterial cells which grow on carbon dioxide, urine, and processed feces. Even without speculating on the catastrophic implications of mutation in *H. eutropha* or on unknown human-produced trace poisons to which Dr. Klein alluded, it is sufficient to note that the NASA system will supply only 85 percent of an astronaut's daily diet. The other 15 percent still must come from stored foods.

The closed system, as defined in NASA's study, is, "Recovery of oxygen, water, and food from wastes; food supplement is provided." So in fact this projected closed system is slightly open.

This is not to cavil at NASA; the system is adequate for the intended voyages. Nor is it said to disparage the spirit or ingenuity of man, traits that hardly have been neglected in song and press release. It is simply cited as a basis for comparison to a life-support system that is self-building, self-evolving, self-repairing, self-perpetuating; that has safely navigated the inimical environment of space for eons; that instead of carbohydrates and bacterial cells provides lobsters and champagne, coffee and cream, bread and apples; that is a completely closed system with myriad components dovetailing; that, in contrast to the 675,000 combinations posited for a man-made spaceship, would overload the most resourceful computer asked to write the equation for one day's interactions.

That system is our planet, earth, and these systemic inter-relationships are what ecology is all about.

In order to make clear to his students what ecology is and where its limits are, Eugene P. Odum in his textbook *Fundamentals of Ecology* divides the biological spectrum into ten levels of organization of life. From the largest unit of organization (that we know) to the smallest, they are:

1. Biosphere
2. Ecosystems
3. Communities
4. Populations
5. Organisms
6. Organ systems
7. Organs
8. Tissues
9. Cells
10. Protoplasm

Ecology, Professor Odum says, usually deals with the top part of the scale—from populations upward. He goes on, "Since introductory biology courses usually stop abruptly with the organism, and since in dealing with man and higher animals, we are accustomed to think of the individual as the ultimate unit, the idea of a continuous spectrum may seem strange at first. However, from the standpoint of interdependence, interrelations and survival, there can be no sharp break anywhere along the line."

It is this different way of looking at units—as interrelated individuals, as interdependent groups, as systems, as functioning wholes—that forms a basic divergence from man's other disciplines and his conventional attitudes.

The biosphere defines the physical limits to where life exists—from a few feet under the soil, the lithosphere, and from the bottom of the ocean, the hydrosphere, into the atmosphere. Since life is found from the ocean's bottom to an altitude of about 22,000 feet above its surface, the biosphere is a band of life about 11 miles in depth. The sphere of life is like the thin skin on an apple.

Population, as the term is used in ecology, means those members of a particular plant or animal species found in a particular area. A community is the combined group of interacting populations in a particular place.

2

An ecosystem—an ecological system—combines the biotic community with the *a*biotic or non-living environment in a particular place as a unit of interrelated life. The physical environment may be regarded as the matrix for the community, although the living species themselves help form the total environment.

To some extent, an ecosystem is an abstraction. The way to look at it is like a box: the ecologist is concerned not only with what is inside the box but what is going into it and what is coming out of it.

The ecosystem idea was expressed back in 1887 by an entomologist in Illinois, Stephen Forbes, who wrote, "A lake . . . forms a little world within itself—a microcosm within which all the elemental forces are at work and the play of life goes on in full, but on so small a scale as to bring it within the mental grasp."

As a unit, an ecosystem can be as small as a fallen tree trunk or as large as the world. But the disadvantage of studying the whole earth as an ecosystem, as Forbes implied, is that it contains an unmanageable amount of information. At least no ecologist has undertaken such an investigation, yet. Ecosystems can overlap, obviously—the forest system would include many smaller ecosystems of fallen trees, the soil, springs, ponds, streams, and enclaves of less typical trees. A city is an ecosystem, but ecology was built on studies of natural systems, and that is where its fundamentals are.

So let us imagine a forest ecosystem: mature sugar maples and beech trees, an occasional hemlock or birch reaching up into the forest canopy, creating the same evanescent interplay of sunlight and leaves that the French Impressionists tried to preserve on canvas. Beneath the dominant trees are other species and adolescents, then shrubs, and along the forest floor herbs, ferns, mosses, lichens, and the litter of fallen leaves. Scarlet tanagers (if you could see them) flash among the treetops where flying squirrels are sleeping. Wood peewees live under the penthouses and below them a red-eyed vireo. Woodpeckers drill tree trunks, nuthatches scout the limbs. In an open grassy field a robin hops along listening for earthworms. At the edge of the clearing, deer browse on a tasty brush; nearby pellets of deer dung are being consumed by invisible microorganisms. The tiny corpse of a baby thrush that fell or was pushed from its nest is being buried by sexton beetles. Nearby a green caterpillar munches on a leaf while a spider spins its web. In the soil are billions of mites, other arthropods, and bacteria. A cowbird flies by seeking the vireo's nest in which to deposit an egg. A family of foxes sleeps in its den, the remains of a rabbit lying with them. By a stream, a dragonfly falls victim to a previously invisible frog which even now is being stalked by a water snake. In a branch overhead, a kingfisher waits, motionless; in a cold brook below, a young trout, melting into the rippling tawny bottom, also waits. Overhead a hawk (yes, one still exists) circles.

That is the structure of the forest ecosystem, but what is the forest *doing?* With all of man's curiosity, with all of his pursuits, no other science has ever asked that question. Ecology's answer is: It is surviving.

It does so on a long-term basis by making the most efficient use possible of the sun's energy and the earth's resources while remaining in equilibrium with its environment. Such a description would still hold if we put a primitive man in the forest—the original Indian inhabitants or tribes that live still in the Brazilian rain forest. Every time a bolt of lightning or careless cigarette ignites a fire, this storehouse of energy is opened like Pandora's box. Meantime, in a less discernible way, the energy is being distributed and the resources recycled through the plant and animal members of what has evolved over many millions of years into a complex organization.

3

In constructing this organization, nature is going counter to the stream of the universe; it is a salmon swimming against a cosmic current.

The solar system is wearing down, going from greater to lesser organization, moving toward an ever greater randomness that is known as entropy. We see a one-way stream of solar energy from our sun. Matter within the sun is transformed into energy which is radiated into space. Over a sufficiently long period of time, the sun's matter-energy will be distributed through space in an unuseable evenness and the sun will be nearly exhausted. This physical process is described by the two great laws of thermodynamics. The first law says that energy is neither created nor destroyed, it is simply transferred from one type to another. The second law says that when energy is transferred, some of it takes a form (such as heat) that cannot be passed on again. This law ordains the eventual exhaustion of the sun and the one-way direction of energy.

Of the sun's tremendous radiant emanation, only about one 50-millionth of the effusion strikes earth. About half of this radiation is in the visible spectrum, most of the rest in the infrared and ultraviolet ranges. The latest scientific observations measure solar energy reaching earth at just under two (1.94) calories a square centimeter a minute, a calorie being a measure of energy (the amount of heat needed to raise one gram of water one degree centigrade). More than half of the incoming solar energy is reflected back out into space by clouds and dust or absorbed in the atmosphere. The rest of it goes to heat the planet. In the long run as much energy leaves the earth as it receives. Of the radiant energy striking earth, only eight percent finally reaches plants—and one-fifth of this is reflected away or passes through. Of what remains, only half is in the visible spectrum that can be utilized by chlorophyll for photosynthesis.

In the highly complex photosynthetic process, green plants fix the radiant energy by converting carbon dioxide and water into carbohydrates, fats, and proteins—chemical energy—giving off oxygen as a waste product. When animals graze upon the plants and in turn are consumed by other animals, the chemical energy is transformed to mechanical energy and heat in cellular metabolism. Energy in biological systems goes by the name of food. The web of nature is linked by stomachs. When the King asked Hamlet where the dead Polonius was, Hamlet replied, "At supper."

"At supper! Where?"

"Not where he eats," said Hamlet, "but where he is eaten. A certain convocation of worms are at him. We fat all creatures else to fat us, and fat ourselves for maggots."

The ecologist's description of the energy dynamics of ecosystems is translated in terms of nutrition; the important ecological term *trophic* stands for food or nourishment. From a basic functioning standpoint, an ecosystem has two trophic categories—autotrophic, for self-nourishing organisms, and heterotrophic, for other-feeding creatures. The heterotrophic realm is divided into several distinctive stages, and all these links in the energy chain are known as trophic levels.

The first trophic level is represented by *producers*. On land, these are the autotrophic green plants capable of fixing radiant energy and manufacturing food for themselves and basically for all other life. The autotrophs in water are minute floating plants, called phytoplankton—*phyto* for plant. While not normally visible to the naked eye, phytoplankton in sufficient quantity can give water a greenish color. Since phytoplankton produce oxygen like green land plants, and since oceans cover 70 percent of the surface of the planet, these waterborne plants are a major source for replenishing the world's oxygen supply. However, since these sea plants are less than land plants in mass, ecologist Robert Whittaker recently calculated that land plants produce a greater amount of oxygen although the contribution of phytoplankton is substantial.

All other organisms are heterotrophs—they feed on plants or other animals. At the second trophic level are *consumers*. And there is a hierarchy among them. Primary consumers are those animals that feed on plants and are known as herbivores. They serve the important function of converting energy to animal tissue while at the same time managing to be so numerous that they support all the animals above them in the food pyramid. On land, primary consumers are insects, rodents, and hoofed animals. In water, primary consumers are zooplankton, crustaceans,

ENERGY FLOW AND THE CLOSED SYSTEM

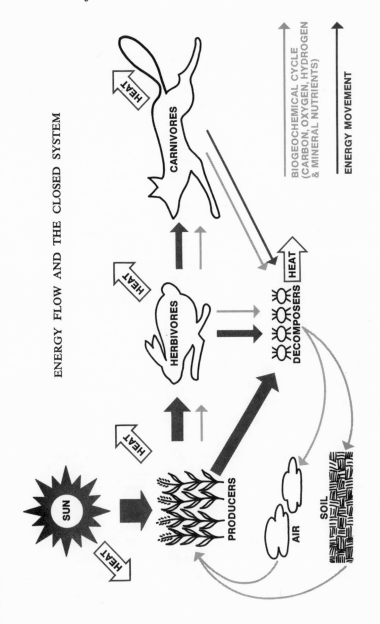

and bottom animals. Plankton, as the foundation of all marine life, sometimes are referred to as the wheat of the sea.

Herbivores, in turn, are eaten by secondary consumers, or carnivores. The shrew that eats a grasshopper is a first-level carnivore. The marsh hawk that eats the shrew is a second-level carnivore. However, the food web is not always a one-track route. For example, the grasshopper may be eaten by a sparrow which is eaten by a Norway rat which is eaten by the marsh hawk. In this case, the hawk becomes a tertiary carnivore. We are familiar with many of the carnivores as predators—foxes and wolves, lions and tigers, hawks and eagles. These animals generally are larger than their prey and come equipped with sharp teeth or talons, great speed, and alertness.

Some animals are specialists, others are generalists. The specialist, such as the previously mentioned Canada lynx, feeds on one particular prey and is well adapted and very efficient in doing that. Generalists—the fox is a good example—can live off a variety of animals as well as carrion. The generalist has the greater chance for survival since his welfare is not tied directly to any one particular species on the trophic levels below him. Certain generalists are known as omnivores—animals that eat plants as well as other animals. Well-known omnivores are bears, pigs, rats, and humans.

These linkages of the food web can be quite intricate and reveal unsuspected ecological relationships when man interferes with nature in blunderbuss fashion. In Borneo, the World Health Organization began a mosquito control program, spraying large amounts of DDT to combat malaria. The campaign proved to be quite effective, but the killing of mosquitoes wasn't the only thing that happened.

The DDT was sprayed inside natives' homes, particularly on walls. Public health officers knew that after feasting on the human host, the female *Anopheles* mosquito, heavy with blood, had a habit of resting on a nearby wall before journeying back home. That contact with DDT was all it took to eliminate the malaria carrier. The DDT also poisoned houseflies. The housefly happens to be a favorite food of a tiny lizard known as the gecko. Geckos ate the flies and died from the DDT. House cats ate the geckos and in turn were poisoned. So many cats were lost that the homes were invaded by rats—and the community was confronted by the threat of another disease, bubonic plague, which is carried by rat fleas.

On top of that, the roofs of the natives' houses began to fall in. In addition to mosquitoes, houseflies, geckos, and cats, the DDT killed great numbers of wasps that preyed on caterpillars. With their predators gone, the caterpillars multiplied, and the lot of them proceeded to dine on their *pièce de résistance*—thatched roofs.

In 1952, French authorities decided to reduce the rabbit population in that country and introduced a highly virulent disease, myxomatosis. The disease reached Kent, England, in 1953, and by 1955 rabbits were almost extinct over most of Britain. The disappearance of the rabbits produced dramatic changes in British vegetation, changes that scientists had not anticipated. Plants that had been contained by the rabbits' appetites suddenly flourished and spread across the land. Fields that once supported a mat of low mosses became covered with thick coats of grass and stands of heather. Other flowering plants disappeared with the rabbits. These changes in the community of plants had profound effects upon insects; similarly, foxes and other predators on the rabbits also were affected in their numbers and feeding habits.

The final link in the food web—the trophic level after producers and consumers—is formed by *decomposers*. Decomposers, in contrast to most other heterotrophs, consist mainly of microorgasmic bacteria and fungi. While some bacteria, as we know, attack living things and can be pathogenic, most bacterial forms feed on dead matter. This consumption, unlike that of other herbivores or carnivores, is not by eating but by absorption. No single species of decomposer accomplishes the breakdown; the job is done assembly line fashion by populations of decomposer specialists. It can be seen that *H. eutropha*, the bacteria being used in the NASA experiments, serves the double purpose of decomposing metabolic wastes while producing consumable protoplasm. Decomposer organisms have high rates of metabolism, which accounts for the extra heat radiating from a pile of cow dung in a field. While decomposers can handle fats, sugars, and proteins with dispatch, they cannot break down plant cellulose and the hair and bones of animals as readily.

So while land plants and phytoplankton are busily manufacturing material for the community, decomposers are just as diligently disposing of it. Who is to say which is more indispensable? All other organisms ultimately depend upon plants for food, of course, but it does not take much imagination to envision the horrible fate that would overtake us if decomposers proved allergic to one of our indiscriminately broadcast pesticides or herbicides. The closed system suddenly would open like a cornucopia to disgorge a torrent of immortal cadavers and non-decaying feces. Indeed, these bacteria are employed under controlled conditions in today's secondary sewage treatment plants.

The chaparral country along the coast of Southern California is an example of what happens when decomposers do not keep up with natural productivity. This semi-arid landscape of shrub and scrub trees experiences long, dry summers. Since microbial decomposers are limited by dryness, the fallen leaves, dead twigs, and branches accumulate. After a certain number of years, the litter reaches such proportions that, in the tinder-dry conditions of mid to late autumn, it is subject to periodic fires. Rangers tried to suppress these fires only to discover that postponement brought more ravaging burns.

In chaparral, fire acts as a decomposer. But this is a rather expensive method of removal since the community must start over again. In this way, fire molds the character of chaparral, favoring faster-growing shrubs and militating against mature trees.

But the fires do release nutrients tied up in the dead organic matter. And this is another vital function of decomposers. Through decomposition, mineral nutrients locked in organic matter once again are returned to the soil where they can be reabsorbed into new plants.

All along the line, the heterotrophs are taking in oxygen given off by green plants and returning carbon dioxide essential for the plants' photosynthesis in a happy exchange. If there is an even-steven trade between oxygen and carbon dioxide, why is air composed of nearly 21 percent oxygen and only about .03 percent carbon dioxide? According to scientific theory, there was little if any oxygen in the atmosphere until the appearance of plant life. Even with the marine photosynthesizers at the beginning, there was negligible buildup of oxygen because of the oxidation of minerals and because whatever surplus oxygen was created by a plant was used up again with the decomposition of that plant. But some of the organisms escaped decomposition by becoming isolated in sedimentary rocks and through geologic processes were transmuted into coal and oil. This reduction in decomposition enabled a gradual expansion of atmospheric oxygen, until about 400 million years ago when the amount of oxygen in the air reached its present level.

It is worth noting here that when we burn these fossil fuels we are cashing the energy saved by living organisms hundreds of millions of years ago and long deposited in the vaults of the earth. These fuels represent earth's accumulated biological capital.

The oxygen-carbon dioxide ratio apparently has remained constant for a very long time, indicating an equilibrium that must have great biological importance. No scientist knows what would happen if this balance is seriously disturbed, which accounts for the uneasiness of ecologists at the tremendous release of carbon dioxide from combustion of fossil fuels and added oxygen demand of internal combustion engines together with the contraction of oxygen-producing green areas (in the United States alone the conversion to paved and urban surfaces occurs at the rate of five million acres a year).

While we are accustomed to thinking of the interactions of environment and life as a one-way affair with environment always determining and molding the form of life, here is an instance of life affecting environment—actually creating an environment highly favorable to perpetuating existence. In addition to supporting animal life the oxygen in the atmosphere filters out lethal ultraviolet rays.

Since photosynthesis and respiration are the biological processes that maintain the balance of atmospheric oxygen and carbon dioxide, we should look more closely at these processes.

Through respiration, an organism oxidizes food in order to procure the energy necessary to carry on its activities— growth, repair, work, reproduction. The by-products of this biochemical process are carbon dioxide and water. In humans these wastes are given off through exhalation in breathing, through perspiration, and through excretion. The importance of perspiration was given dramatic acknowledgment in the film *Goldfinger* when a woman was murdered by painting her entire body with gold.

Plants, like animals, also use oxygen and give off carbon dioxide in respiration in order to supply the energy needed for growth, maintenance, and photosynthesis. This drain on oxygen underlies the old custom of removing plants and flowers from a sickroom or bedroom at night. But plants operate efficiently, and photosynthesis during the daytime produces much more fixed energy, and gives off more oxygen as a by-product, than plant respiration consumes.

4

Through photosynthesis, the metabolic opposite of respiration, a plant captures energy through the manufacture of protoplasm. In other words, energy is turned back into matter. This conversion offers ecologists a convenient way to measure how and how much energy is being utilized. They simply weigh all the organisms of one or all species in a given area. This total amount of living weight of a species within an area or ecosystem is known as *biomass*. If you would think of the aggregate of all human flesh, bones, juices, and hair—putting on one giant scale all the rumps and breasts, limbs and viscera—the total would be the biomass for *Homo sapiens*. The minute by minute growth of this biomass with increasing world population is a measure of the ever larger amount of energy being incorporated by this species.

Ecologists, until quite recently, have been mainly concerned with other species. They were interested in knowing, first, how much total energy a plant captured from the radiant stream. This is called gross primary production. One is struck immediately by how little of the available solar energy a plant uses—two percent or less (and we already have seen what a small fraction of the incoming radiant energy is available to plants).

Edgar Transeau, studying a Midwestern corn field, found that 1.6 percent of the available solar energy was converted into food tissue. The corn plant required one quarter of that for its own purposes. The remainder is known as net primary production and eventually every bit of it passes through the living community. Man, of course, harvests the corn ears so we might think of that as net primary production. But the ecologist considers roots, stalks, leaves, litter—the total amount of organic tissue.

Ecologists have drawn a profile of nature's productivity by measuring the biomass produced per square meter per day in a variety of ecosystems. Professor Eugene Odum has described this graduated scale of productivity. Deserts and the open ocean are least productive with increments of one-half a gram or less of biomass a day. In the next category, producing from one-half to three grams of biomass a day, are grasslands, continental shelf waters, mountain forests, and some agriculture. Producing three to ten grams a day are moist forests and young forests, shallow lakes, moist grasslands, and moist agriculture. The most productive areas, yielding from ten to twenty-five grams a day, are salt marshes, estuaries, coral reefs, springs, terrestrial communities on river banks, mangrove swamps, and intensive year-round agriculture.

Twenty-five grams of biomass per square meter a day appears to be an upper limit of sustained production for any ecosystem, natural or cultivated. Investigators have found that man has not increased maximum primary production beyond that which occurs naturally. The use of fertilizers and irrigation simply have made up for potentially limiting factors in the production.

There are two kinds of chains by which this net primary production spreads through the food web. We, of course, are most conscious of the grazing-predator chain since we are a part of it. But energy also is stored in undecomposed leaves and other dead organic matter and then transferred directly to decay microorganisms. Lately, researchers have discovered that in many ecosystems, a very large proportion of the energy passes through the detritus or decay chain. Detritus is dead organic matter and a good example of it is seen in the litter of leaves in a woodland. Trees and plants molt much as animals do. One study in Europe revealed that only about seven percent of the annual crop of forest leaves was eaten on the tree; the other 93 percent was eaten by detritus consumers and decomposers. A study of Root Spring in Concord, Massachusetts, by John Teal showed that photosynthesis accounted for only one-quarter of the energy funneled into the spring ecosystem. The rest entered in the form of debris falling on the spring from trees and plants. Most of the life in the Root Spring ecosystem was supported by energy from imported dead material.

Ecologists today regard an ecosystem's metabolism much in the way a physician or physiologist would look at an individual's metabolism. If the expenditure of energy through respiration exceeds the production through photosynthesis, then the imbalance must be made up from energy entering from outside the ecosystem, as in Root Spring, from past production, stored capital, or else the ecosystem must reduce its activity. In a study of simplified ecosystems, Robert Byers found on the average that photosynthesis slightly exceeded respiration. And an experiment by B. J.

Copeland showed that when the input of light was cut by five-sixths, the ecosystem's metabolic activity was reduced by a similar amount. The point is, in nature's system, no credit is extended and no national debt is allowed.

Indeed, as weight watchers know, there can be no cheating in the transaction between caloric income and expenditure. If a person takes in more energy than he uses, then the energy must be stored as fat. If he consumes more energy than he supplies, he grows thin. If the imbalance persists, the person becomes emaciated and finally dies. While death from starvation can be a fate common to all animals, have you wondered that you never see overweight wild specimens? Obesity is compatible only with civilization. In natural systems, the penalty for overeating is not corpulence but extinction. The fat cat cannot catch his prey. The fat prey cannot elude his predator. Some insects automatically turn any excess energy into greater reproduction.

A study of an old field community in southern Michigan gives a good illustration of what happens to energy as it passes through the ecosystem, in this case along the grazing-predator chain—from vegetation to herbivorous meadow mice to carnivorous weasels. The mice ate two percent of the plant tissue available to them and used two-thirds of the assimilated energy for respiration. Weasels ate about 31 percent of the mice and used 93 percent of their energy for life maintenance. So little energy remained that no secondary carnivore could exist on weasels alone.

It is interesting to see the gradations of animal populations according to their rung on the trophic ladder or position on the energy line. Using the yardstick of biomass, which takes into account both the size of the animal as well as its numbers, typical herbivores out-thrive most carnivores by a factor of 100 or even 1,000. Even among herbivores, there is a noticeable difference between animals that eat foliage and those that consume seeds and fruits. The foliage eaters—such as deer, woodchucks, and voles—on the average have twice the biomass of seed and fruit eaters such as squirrels, chipmunks, and mice. The foliage eaters have a biomass ten times as great as the black bear and 100 times that of two other omnivores, foxes and skunks. As for the carnivores—the cougar, lynx, and weasel—they had a total of living weight ten times less than the skunk and fox, 100 times less than the black bear, and 1,000 times less than the foliage eating deer and groundhogs.

This energy loss at each transfer is still in obedience to the second law of thermodynamics. While there is considerable variability in what Lawrence B. Slobodkin calls gross ecological efficiency, he suggests that it is of the order of ten percent. If there are 1,000 calories of net plant production, 100 calories would be consumed at the herbivore level, ten calories at the carnivore level, one calorie by the secondary carnivore, and one-tenth of a calorie by the tertiary carnivore—which explains why there is rarely a fifth link in the food chain, and why there are so few members of the species at the top of natural food pyramids—eagles, hawks, panthers. It also explains why man has never lived off the major predators. The animals we do eat are herbivores, although the omnivorous pig is a most efficient converter among farm animals. Perhaps as much as 20 percent of the energy fed to a pig is eaten by man.

The geometric energy loss shows why people in poor and populous countries must shorten their food chain, must be herbivores, must subsist on rice, corn, soybeans, or other plants. The energy reduction from plant to beef to man is about the same as it is for plant to meadow mouse to weasel. The amount of cultivated land required to produce a pound of steak is clearly an unacceptable luxury where many people go hungry. A 10-acre field produces the plant fodder to provide enough beef to feed one person for a year. The same field could produce sufficient rice to feed two dozen people for a year.

5

While energy is moving continuously through the ecosystem, becoming dissipated and finally lost completely, the materials of the system are recirculating. Carbon is needed with water's hydrogen and oxygen to make energy-storing carbohydrates and fats. Nitrates and phosphates are essential to plant growth. Magnesium is a necessary constituent of chlorophyll. Potassium, sulfur, and calcium are other elements needed in large amounts by living systems. Nitrogen, phosphorous, potassium, sulfur, calcium, and magnesium are known as macronutrients. But plants also need small amounts of other minerals such as iron, manganese, molybdenum, copper, zinc, cobalt, boron, sodium, chlorine, and vanadium. These are called micronutrients. Most living organisms require more than thirty elements that are *essential* to their growth and development. Man biologically needs forty elements.

These chemical nutrients circulate continuously through the biological organisms and the geological matrix of the ecosystem in what is known as the *biogeochemical cycle*. The water cycle is most commonly known to us. Seventy-five percent of our protoplasm is water. Water vapor enters the air from our bodies through our exhalation or perspiration, from bodies of water through evaporation and from plants through transpiration (the passage of vapor through tissue). The vapor forms clouds, the water descends in precipitation to be taken up by plants or else it runs off as surface water to enter lakes and oceans; or it percolates down through the soil to be taken up by plants or to reach the ground water that humans drink or that eventually reaches plants or bodies of surface water.

A few biogeochemical cycles are called gaseous cycles because the environmental home of the element is the atmosphere. Carbon and oxygen are two of these elements. So huge is the movement of carbon that it has been estimated that from 45 to 100 billion tons of the element move through the biosphere each year.

The nitrogen cycle is far more complicated. While nitrogen is a requisite of all life and is most plenteous (about 78 percent) in the atmosphere, it cannot be used in its gaseous form by plants. It must first be changed into an inorganic form, mainly nitrate. This transformation is generally brought about by nitrogen fixers, different species of bacteria, fungi, and algae. One group of these nitrogen fixers is composed of bacteria and some fungi species that live in symbiotic association with the roots of legumes, such as peas, clover, and beans. The other group of bacteria or algae live free in soil or water. Since nitrogen is essential to photosynthesis, the amount of nitrate in the soil can be a regulating factor in the growth of crops—and explains why the addition of artificial nitrate fertilizer promotes a greater yield.

In living organisms, the nitrogen is incorporated in protein and nucleic acids. It leaves the living community either as part of dead organic matter or as urea in body wastes, which is why animal manure has served so well as natural fertilizer.

The bacterial decomposers consume the organic nitrogen along with other dead matter, and reconvert it to an inorganic form, ammonia. Then one group of so-called nitrifying bacteria transforms the ammonia to nitrite, a toxic compound, while a second group completes the process back to nitrate. These nitrifying bacteria, which are one-celled plants, are autotrophs like green plants, but manufacture their own food in the absence of sunlight in a process called chemosynthesis. The conversion of ammonia to nitrite and nitrate is part of the chemosynthetic process.

In the form of nitrate, the nitrogen once again can be assimilated by green plants or be subject to a group of *de*nitrifying bacteria that can reduce the nitrate back to nitrite or others that change it back to ammonia or still *other* denitrifying bacteria that return the nitrogen to its gaseous state where it is a candidate once again for nitrogen-fixing bacteria.

The process is more complicated and delicately balanced than this simplified outline indicates. For instance, investigations have shown that the presence or absence of phosphorous and other macronutrients controls the capacity of nitrogen-fixing organisms, thus regulating the production of nitrate which itself is a regulator of photosynthesis.

While some nitrogen is being lost to deep ocean sediments for perhaps millions of years, an equivalent amount of new molecular nitrogen is fed into the cycle from volcanic gases. With the various feedback and compensatory mechanisms, the nitrogen system is a recycling marvel.

Phosphorous, sulfur, iron, potassium, and similar nutrients pass through what is known as the sedimentary cycle, since these elements reside in the earth when they are not constituents of living matter. In general, these nutrients do not circulate with the ease of carbon and have fewer self-correcting mechanisms than nitrogen. And so there is a tendency for some of them to stagnate for short or indefinite periods of time. Phosphorous, critical for metabolic energy transfer and genetic coding, apparently is being lost to the deep ocean sediments at a much faster rate than nitrogen. While there is no present shortage of phosphate rock, eventually, the drain could pose a problem for all life. The time could come when men will look back in angry despair at our profligate manufacture, sale, and use of phosphate detergents.

Still, the wonder is how perfectly the biogeochemical cycle has resupplied life for hundreds of millions of years and distributed these essential nutrients so well that living systems can function almost everywhere on the planet.

One implication of the endless recycling of these indestructible elements is a sort of molecular reincarnation. Carbon or calcium molecules in your body once may have belonged to *Tyrannosaurus rex*, or a rose, to Kilimanjaro or Leonardo.

But there is another and far more threatening meaning. Any substance introduced into the environment, if it is durable, is eligible for the biogeochemical cycle. If that substance is introduced in sufficient quantity, it can pervade the earth's ecosystems.

Although lead is lethal to most living creatures in extremely small amounts, it never was a ubiquitous hazard as a naturally occurring element until man made it airborne and available to the biogeochemical cycle. Today, it is estimated that the atmosphere of the northern hemisphere contains about a thousand times more than the natural amount of lead. Corings in snow near the North Pole by Clair Patterson of California Institute of Technology show that lead concentration quadrupled between 1750, when lead smelting increased with the Industrial Revolution, and 1940. Between 1940, when leaded gasoline became widely used, until 1965 the concentration again increased between two and a half and three times. In the United States, lead content in blood ranges from .05 parts per million to .4 parts per million in some urban workers, with a mean level of .25 parts per million. In children, .6 parts per million indicates clinical lead poisoning and when blood lead content reaches that level in an industrial worker, he usually is removed from occupational exposure. No one knows the implications or penalty for carrying a lead burden 100 times what is considered normal for a lifetime.

Radioactivity also occurs naturally in small amounts. But with the nuclear bombs of the 1940s, 1950s, and 1960s, man introduced massive amounts of long-lasting strontium-90 and cesium-137 into the environment. In some areas, depending upon the biological systems and the biogeochemical cycle, the buildup of radioactivity was gradual. In the Arctic, the fallout was heavy, the dominant vegetation, lichen, absorbs virtually all radioactive particles, and the food chain is short. The result is that humans accumulated one-third to one-half the permissable amounts of radiocontamination, attaining a level that could produce physical and genetic damage.

It is because of biogeochemical cycling that DDT sprayed in an Indian hut to kill *Anopheles* mosquitoes, or laid down on a California farm to kill cotton pests, appears in penguins in Antarctica and in human mother's milk in New York City.

Because of increasing DDT levels, it is calculated that the Bermuda petrel will cease reproducing by 1978. The species will become extinct. There aren't many of these petrels and, as today's hard-nosed realists like to point out, species have been going out of business for a long time. But to George Woodwell, the Bermuda petrel is as much a harbinger as the dove was to Noah or the vulture to less fortunate men.

Dr. Woodwell, senior ecologist at Brookhaven National Laboratory, knows that the Bermuda petrel feeds on the open Atlantic Ocean and if that bird, at the top of its food chain, is stricken with DDT then the ocean's living creatures must be burdened by the nerve toxin. This petrel is not an isolated case, however. Pelicans off California are doomed, the nesting peregrine falcon is gone from the United States east of the Rockies, many species of hawks are in sharp decline in the northern hemisphere.

"These bird populations are but one sign that biological systems all over the world are being affected by current levels of DDT," Dr. Woodwell said in the spring of 1969. "If we go on for another 25 or 50 years, we will certainly lose our oceanic fisheries. Many of the food fish that we now harvest will no longer be there because of failure of reproduction due to the accumulation of persistent pesticides."

Dr. Woodwell expects drastic changes sooner, however, and when pressed, says it is not inconceivable that these persistent poisons already may be causing fish population declines. In the summer of 1969, the jack mackerel catch off Southern California—an entire fishery—was condemned by the Food and Drug Administration for pesticide pollution. We know that the DDT cannot get to the mackerel or the petrel or pelican without passing through the phytoplankton upon which we rely for oxygen.

Of course, our survival depends just as absolutely upon those bacteria in the nitrogen cycle or counterparts in the sulfur cycle or the decomposer microorganisms or the availability of phosphorous and potassium and molybdenum. We humans are one of many way stations in the biogeochemical system, unable to shut off the current if it is injurious to us, even if it becomes lethal. We are but one major strand in the food web, incapable of making our own biological energy.

So the science of ecology finally enables us to perceive the hidden imperative in John Donne's admonition, "Therefore never send to know for whom the bell tolls . . ."

That is the meaning of the closed system.

CHAPTER THREE

The Stable System

1

THE EARTH ROTATES about its axis and there is day and night. The earth revolves around the sun, and because the planet's axis is inclined to the plane of revolution, the length of day ceaselessly oscillates, the sun's direct rays swing across the sphere north and south, south and north like a moving searchlight. In Northern and Southern Hemispheres the temperature rises and falls in cyclic regularity; the seasons change in reverse order for each hemisphere. The earth has mass and therefore gravity. The lunar satellite exerts its own pull as it orbits its spinning captor.

To each of these forces the tapestry of life responds with an infinity of accommodations, adjustments, and adaptations. The tapestry itself is one variegated response to its physical circumstances. But while tapestry is a useful image in that it suggests woven strands arranged in patterns subtly blending into a finely designed fabric, the analogy is misleading in a basic way. It implies a static entity. The living tapestry is vibrant. The terrestrial composition and appearance are ever changing: deciduous forests bright with the slow-motion flames of autumn, conifers a deeper green against winter's white, tides relentlessly advancing and receding, waves snapping at sandy beaches, the animals' comings and goings spatially and temporally, the quality of light endlessly modified by clouds.

Perhaps a more helpful metaphor would be to compare the aggregate of life to music—a complex symphony in which the notes and melodies, chords and arpeggios, counterpoints and harmonies, tempos and rhythms are an orchestrated response to physical reality.

Indeed, life is so entwined with the realities of earth's behavior in the universe that the rhythms are incorporated into the biological systems. Plants must work during the day, of course, in order to utilize sunlight. Bees and moths must call when flowers are open for business. Predators must obey the timetable of their prey. Cheetahs, for instance, migrate with the gazelles. Other environmental changes accompany the light of day—the temperature rises and the air grows drier. Centipedes and millipedes, which lose moisture rapidly when exposed to dry air, flee to dark dampness under rocks and leaves to emerge once again at dusk.

All creatures live by a 24-hour routine. At first, investigators believed that these daily activities were solely determined by external stimuli such as a change of light intensity, temperature, or moisture. Then they discovered that the various species carry their own biological clocks. And the one that governs the 24-hour pattern is called the circadian rhythm—*circa* is Latin for about, and *dies* is Latin for day.

Airplane travelers notice their circadian rhythm when they fly to a land that is bustling with mid-afternoon activity while their own bodies tell them it is bedtime. Ralph Schoenstein, a freelance travel writer, underwent what must be circadian fibrillation when he jetted around the Southern Hemisphere in ten days, alighting at various points for a few hours. "I arrived in Johannesburg in midday, but I really didn't know what time it was or where I was because, you see, I had just been in Sydney five thousand miles away where I already had lost track of my schedule. It took me a week to get back into sync."

The working of circadian rhythm is imperfectly understood. A report in November, 1969, by the President's Science Advisory Committee says that in order to undertake extended space flights, extensive investigation must be devoted to finding the limits of human biological capability. The report asserts that virtually nothing is known about the limits of muscular work in the weightless state, and goes on; "Little data has been gathered on changes in circadian and other biological rhythms, although astronauts have encountered significant difficulties in sleeping."

Studies on human subjects who have lived in caves or otherwise been isolated from the outside world show definite circadian rhythms for sleep and wakefulness, body temperature, volume of urine excretion, and contents of potassium and calcium. The peaks of most human rhythms come during the day, a fact well known by anyone who has worked the midnight to eight A.M. shift. We are diurnal animals.

It is interesting to note that humans isolated from the outside daily cycle of light and darkness, and clocks, tend to live in a cycle that averages 25 hours—a rhythm that in less than two weeks would put them diametrically out of phase with their normal routine. This and other findings tell investigators that animals live according to internal rhythms, but they continually check and reset their biological clocks by environmental signals.

Because of circadian rhythm, very few Americans have ever seen one of the most common mammals in the United

States, the flying squirrel. It lives in the tops of trees and comes out at night. It is a nocturnal animal. The rat population is estimated to be as large as the human one, yet we rarely see our most important mammal competitor, for it, like the flying squirrel, is a nocturnal rodent.

That fact figured importantly in an early experiment in applied ecology. The black rat, *Rattus rattus*, undoubtedly slipped ashore on Hawaii when Captain James Cook first called in 1778, to be followed by the more aggressive brown or Norway rat. The largest native animal on the islands was the smaller Hawaiian rat and so the newcomers proceeded to take over and to multiply. While the three species of rats coexist on Hawaii, the Norway brown rats dominate; the black rats, retreating before their fiercer cousins, largely took to the trees.

A conflict over Hawaiian fields developed in the middle of the 19th century when men decided to grow sugar cane and resented sharing profits with the rats. Plantation owners tried different methods to eliminate the by then very numerous rodents, without success.

Then, in 1883, owners tried what today is called biological control. They imported 36 pairs of mongooses. In its native India where it is readily domesticated the mongoose is famous for dueling with poisonous snakes. But the mammal, which can grow to a length of four feet including its tail, also feeds on rodents. And that was the strategy behind the Hawaiian experiment.

The mongooses were liberated on Hawaii, writes William Alanson Bryan in his *Natural History of Hawaii,* "in the hope that they would be of value in freeing the cane fields of rats. Unfortunately, they were carried from one island to another before their habits were fully understood." Specifically, the mongoose is a diurnal animal; it hunts by day.

The result was that rat and mongoose happily multiplied side by side without seeing one another. Under the circumstances, the wild mongoose—which has a craving for chicken, other ground-nesting birds, and their eggs—was left with no alternative except to make a pest of itself, also. The rats in Hawaii now outnumber humans seven to one and are busy every night eating sugar cane—four and a half million dollars worth annually.

The *length* of day—known to ecologists as the photoperiod—also is important, determining many plants' annual rhythms. Some are known as "long-day" plants which will flower only after the photoperiod exceeds a certain minimum, usually twelve to fourteen hours. "Short-day" plants, conversely, will flower only when the photoperiod is shorter than a certain maximum. The photoperiod requirement may vary within the same species. For instance, the alpine sorrel in Wyoming needs 15 hours of daylight, but in the Arctic needs a 20-hour day in order to bloom.

Brook trout breed in autumn. They respond to short days. Experiments in which light was artificially controlled showed that if day length is first increased, then shortened, the trout can be made to spawn in July. Normally, the breeding condition of the ferret is brought on by an 18-hour photoperiod. But experimenters found that breeding can be induced by exposing the animal to only twelve hours of light each day for a month *providing* that one hour of light is given from midnight to one A.M. Researchers believe that these various light-darkness signals start time-measuring processes in the endocrinal system that then make organisms light-sensitive.

In birds, photoperiodism triggers migration. Such a starting mechanism could account for the precision with which the swallows return to Capistrano—for the annual moment

of the sun's rising is unvarying. It was found that the increasing length of day stimulates the migrating bird's pituitary gland which in turn sets in motion a series of changes
preparing the bird physically for its journey. Finally, this
physiological preparation reaches a threshold that responds
to some environmental change and launches the flight.
Northward migration in spring usually begins with the arrival of a warm front with low barometric pressure and
moist air from the Caribbean or Gulf of Mexico. A cold
front will temporarily stop a migration in mid-flight; it has
even turned flocks southward.

Of course, migration is an exercise in survival. Because
of nesting, the birds would suffer from overcrowding in the
South in summer and would succumb to winter in the
North. Other organisms endure the winter crisis by other
methods. Annual plants survive as seeds. Perennials become
dormant. Dormancy is a common defense. Many species
of insects as well as some crustaceans and snails enter
what is called diapause, a state of dormancy and arrested
growth; frequently in the stage of eggs, larvae or pupae.
Since reptiles and amphibians cannot regulate their internal
temperature, they assume the temperature of their surroundings and hibernate. Snakes seek burrows in rocky hill-
sides, turtles bury themselves in mud and as their body
temperature cools, their heartbeat drops, metabolic rate
slows, and they enter a state of suspended animation. A few
so-called warm-blooded animals, ones that can control their
body temperatures, also survive winter through hibernation.
The woodchuck is one of them.

Some birds—the cardinal, for instance—do not have to
migrate. Ecologist David Gates explains why: "When the
weather is very cold the cardinal turns up its metabolic rate,
tucks its bill under its wing to cut down water-loss rate,

fluffs out its feathers to improve insulation, lifts one leg up under its body, and conserves heat in every possible way. When the air temperature is — 40 degrees Centigrade, the cardinal stays out of the wind; it must do so in order to survive. When the climate is very warm the cardinal must get out of the sun; it turns up its rate of water loss to just match its metabolic rate, which it depresses, and it ventilates as much as possible. The cardinal in deep shade can withstand a maximum air temperature of 42.5 degrees Centigrade and a minimum of — 41 degrees Centigrade (108.5 to — 41 degrees Fahrenheit). Normally, a small animal would have difficulty accepting such an enormous range of air temperature, but because of the fabulous insulation quality of feathers, some birds can meet these extremes."

Dr. Gates and Warren Porter have studied the environmental demands that sunlight, temperature, moisture, and wind put upon various creatures and their ability to respond in terms of expenditure and conservation of energy. This energy is exchanged between the body interior and surface dependent upon the insulation of fat and by fur or feathers. The goal, says Gates, "was to predict the climate space (air temperature, wind, and radiation) which any animal must occupy in order to survive thermodynamically as based on its intrinsic properties." The study included a desert iguana, cow, shrew, pig, jackrabbit, and cardinal, and the predictions came remarkably close to the situations in which these animals actually live.

In the report, "Thermodynamic Equilibria of Animals with Environment," Porter and Gates state, "one of the primary means by which the environment influences animals is through the exchange of energy. If the animal takes in more energy than it gives out it will get warmer, overheat and perish. If the animal loses more energy than it gains it will cool and not survive. An animal may warm or cool for a limited period of time, but on the average, over an extended period of time, an animal must be in energy balance with its environment."

The ecologists note that animals, being mobile, can seek the most compatible environment. Trees cannot move around; they must adjust to their circumstances. In the study of an energy exchange of a pine tree, Dr. Gates and colleagues actually counted the number of needles on the tree—it had 450,000—in order to determine exactly how the tree allocated its material, how much surface it required, how much air flow it needed to stay healthy.

2

It is clear that the configuration of terrestrial life is molded by the powerful triumvirate of sunlight, temperature, and moisture. Since this triad and wind—considered as interacting factors in the Porter/Gates study—constitute climate, a look at weather systems is an instructive introduction to the ecological map of the world.

Even though water passes through biological systems to be used temporarily for protoplasm and life's processes, weather is essentially a physical system. Most of the sunlight reaching the earth's surface provides the energy to heat the land and waters; it causes evaporation and powers ocean currents, breezes, and tornadoes. The earth reflects some of the radiation which then is trapped by water vapor and carbon dioxide in the atmosphere and reradiated both out into space and back to earth. This so-called "greenhouse effect" keeps the earth's temperature about 65 degrees warmer than it ordinarily would be. And the effect also explains why even a slight change in the atmospheric content of CO_2 could exert a profound influence on climate.

The fact is that the amount of carbon dioxide in the air increased by ten percent between 1880 and 1940 and has continued to rise since then. Nevertheless, our average temperature since 1940 has cooled by one half a degree, according to meteorologist Louis J. Battan of the University of Arizona, and that may be because pollution—dust, soot, smoke, and other particulates—in the atmosphere is screening the sunlight and offsetting the greenhouse effect. If by some miracle we were able to remove all atmospheric pollution, but the increased CO_2 remained, we might suddenly find a more tropical tinge to our lives . . . hardly a welcome prospect for coastal areas if the polar icecaps melted. This conjectured dilemma is what can result from tampering with a finely adjusted system.

Evaporation from liquid or plant surface to vapor, condensation from vapor to liquid or plant surface, and precipitation all occur according to physical principles of vapor-pressure ratios and the air's saturation capacity which is related to temperature. As we know, warm air rises, cold air is denser and heavier. From this one might think that cold air continuously generated at the North Pole should bull its way down to the Equator where the heat would elevate the zephyrs for the high road return trip. But it does not work that simply.

The air currents are vertical in the tropical zone, all right, which is why sailing vessels stall in the doldrums. As anyone who has visited the tropics is aware, warm air can hold more moisture than cold air. As this warm moist air rises in the Equatorial zone it cools, loses its saturation capacity, and releases enormous amounts of rain to water the luxuriant tropical rain forests of Brazil, Africa, and Asia.

There is a systemic cleavage at the Equator—the air on the north side proceeds northward, that to the south southward. But it must be remembered that air at the Equator is moving with the earth at about a thousand miles an hour in conformity with the planet's west-to-east rotation. As the air progresses northward the earth's spin decreases, which means that these high volumes of air begin moving faster west-to-east than the ground below. The result is a deflection in the northward wave, a veering toward the east. Losing more warmth and buoyancy, these air masses descend at about 30 to 35 degrees north latitude.

The descending air masses form huge high pressure areas and, warming with their descent, absorb moisture like great atmospheric blotters. Deserts such as the Sahara are the result. Some of the air splashes northward, but much of it turns back toward the Equator.

Now heading southward toward latitudes rotating ever faster, the air masses fall behind the earth's spin and veer toward the west. These are the trade winds sweeping from the northeast; they account for the relatively dry areas in southern and lower California (since the Southern Hemisphere is virtually a mirror image, the great Australian Desert corresponds geographically to the Sahara while the southeast trades cause an arid area on Chile's west coast similar to that of California). These winds pick up moisture as they go along until once again they are blown skyward by the tropical furnace.

The hemispheric division of air currents at the Equator has a meaning for civilization. Most of the planet's land mass is in the Northern Hemisphere. The great preponderance of humans live north of the equator. Virtually all of the high-technology societies are in the Northern Hemisphere. This is the hemisphere where the hydrocarbons, sulfur and nitrogen oxides, soot and radioactive particles, air-borne lead—as Dr. Patterson's corings of arctic snow testify—are thoroughly dispersed.

In latitudes immediately north of the trade winds, the westerlies provide a generous rainfall for most of the West Coast of the United States. As these prevailing winds, in part propelled by the jet stream overhead, hit the succession of western mountain ranges, they are drained of moisture. The air climbs the mountains, cooling as it ascends and losing its capacity to retain moisture so that windward sides of mountains are favored with rain while "rain shadows" develop on the leeward sides. The Great Basin Desert lies between the Sierra and Cascade mountain ranges and the Rockies.

The central area of the United States east of the Rocky Mountains is an arena for contending weather systems—the dessicated westerlies, the clashing polar and tropical currents converging from north and south. The East Coast and Appalachians receive plentiful precipitation from the steadily flowing and now merged westerly system abetted by northeasters and tropical storms that reach titanic expression in hurricanes.

With such diversity of climate, the first Europeans to encounter the continent were confronted with a bewildering abundance and variety. A masterpiece of nature, a huge deciduous forest covered the eastern half of what was to be the United States. To the north the hardwoods melded into evergreen forests. No one knew it then, but civilized men were beholding the world's last great undisturbed hardwood forest. The wonder is how few beholders appreciated what they saw. To the Pilgrims, the wilderness was forboding. But John Brereton, a Cambridge divine landed on Virginia's shore in 1602 and later recorded in his diary:

"On Friday the fourteenth of May, early in the morning, we made land. This island is full of faire trees, of high timbered Oaks; Cedars, strait and tall; Beach, Elme, Hollie, Walnut trees in abundance; Strawberries, red and white, as sweet and much bigger than ours in England. Raspberries, Gooseberries, Hurtleberries, and such. Also many springs of excellent sweet water, which is maintained with the springs running exceeding pleasantly thorow the woodie grounds. This Lake is full of small Tortoises, and exceedingly full of divers fowles as Cranes, Hernshawes, Bitters, Geese; Mallards, Teales, which breed, some lowe on the banks, and others on lowe trees, about this Lake in great abundance, whose young ones of all sorts we tooke and eat at our pleasure. Here are also great stores of Deere, which we saw, and other beasts, as appeared by their tracks. Coming ashore, we stood a while like men ravished at the beautie and delicacie of this sweet soile."

Across the Mississippi and wide Missouri Rivers, a later generation found the prairie, perhaps the world's pre-eminent tall grass area. The pioneers rolled through a sea of magnificent long grass as tall as the wagon wheels, over a man's head. Novelist Willa Cather described the scene in *My Antonia*: "As I looked about me I felt that the grass was the country, as the water is the sea. The red of the grass made all the great prairie the color of winestains, or of certain seaweeds when they are first washed up. And there was so much motion in it; the whole country seemed, somehow, to be running."

Farther west, the buffalo grazed on the short grass that gradually merged into scrub that grudgingly submitted to desert. In the Northwest, mountains and conifers towered into the sky while clustered on the central coast rose the most majestic form of life on the planet, the redwoods.

All these biomes—that is what these major terrestrial ecosystems are called—show a close relationship to annual rainfall. From 30 to 50 inches or more of rain fall evenly on the temperate deciduous forest. The annual rainfall is from 10 to 30 inches for the grasslands; the correspondence holds within the biome: the tall grass to the east gets more rain than the short grass to the west. The deprived deserts usually get less than 10 inches a year. But the belt of conifer trees rimming the West Coast from central California to Alaska may be bathed in more than 100 inches of moisture annually, much of it in the form of soaking summer fogs. The redwoods are at the southern end of what sometimes is called the temperate rain forest. The tropical rain forests luxuriate in 80, 100, and more inches of rain annually.

These correlations have been further refined to show a relationship between biomes and the ratio of precipitation to evaporation. An ecosystem also is influenced by *how* the water is delivered—if the total annual rainfall is deposited in a few cloud bursts, it is not as beneficial as the year-round distribution that nourishes the deciduous forest. Finally, some investigators point out the close correlations of different soils with the major biomes.

With this preface, we can turn to the ecological map of the world. This is a far more accurate or natural representation of our globe than the political maps that we are accustomed to seeing and that have contributed so importantly to our miseducation. Political maps give us an artificial or "unnatural" concept of our world. Who can say how great an influence the centuries of gazing at political maps with their arbitrary colors and concentration on human power have wielded in shaping the present-day world in which we live?

The two kinds of maps exemplify the difference in the

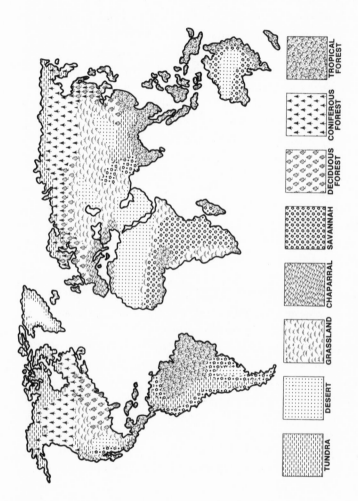

MAJOR BIOMES OF THE WORLD

TUNDRA DESERT GRASSLAND CHAPARRAL SAVANNAH DECIDUOUS FOREST CONIFEROUS FOREST TROPICAL FOREST

ecologists' view and the conventional view of reality. The political map is an anthropocentric representation, human-oriented. It says that certain groups of people own certain territories. It implies that the human species has sovereign rights in those spaces. It disenfranchises the rest of life, assuming that the planet is human property.

The ecological map is closer to what an astronaut sees when he circles overhead, although it does not correspond in every detail with the landscape that exists at any given moment. Rather it is a map of the world's great natural systems as they would be if left alone. The boundaries are determined by climatic or topographical changes. Man, who is just one part of the arrangement, is not directly represented on this map even though his sprawling settlements have replaced natural ecosystems, even though he has enlarged the deserts, even though he has converted grasslands to agricultural systems.

At one time, grasslands covered 42 percent of the land surface of the earth; today much of this area is used for agriculture. In the once continuous forest of the eastern United States there now are gaps for farms and towns and pastures and strip mines. But if the farmer stops his cultivation or the fields are left alone or the towns abandoned for long enough, the land will return to its native natural system, be it grassland or forest.

It can be seen that the biomes of the United States are divided generally along north-south lines, largely because of the moisture gradients and the western mountain ranges. But as we move north, because of temperature the divisions become lateral—first, the moist but cold coniferous forest, the great north woods, and then the tundra. Of course, if we look laterally from the United States, we see that deciduous forests also occur through Europe and Russian Asia and in China; to the north of them is the coniferous forest, and north of that the tundra. There is a stratified consistency to the form biological systems take under increasingly rigorous climates.

To the south, with higher temperatures and increased rainfall the tropical rain forest appears. This is the most complex of all terrestrial biomes; it supports the greatest biomass. In warm regions where there is abundant rainfall but a prolonged dry season, we see a combination of grasslands with scattered trees or clumps of trees. These are known as savannahs, common to the southern half of Africa and indigenous to parts of southeastern United States, as the name Savannah, Georgia, indicates. In temperate areas where winters are mild and summers long and dry, chaparral occurs. This biome rings the Mediterranean Sea.

These are the major land divisions—desert, tundra, grassland, chaparral (shrub-lands), savannah, forest— which along with oceans, lakes, and rivers make up the world ecosystems. They are distinct configurations of life with characteristic constellation of plants and animals (man can be found in them all).

3

Deserts are among the least studied biomes—our ecological ignorance of deserts is exceeded only by that of tropical rain forests. Generally, deserts come about in three ways. They are produced by the subtropical dry and high pressure air masses, by rain shadows from mountains (the Great Basin is an example of a cold desert), and by man. Basically, man-made deserts are evidence of futile attempts to wring more from the land than it could give. The most common methods have been through improperly cultivating arid land and through overgrazing. Often these practices occur in marginal areas adjacent to natural desert and are the reasons why the Sahara has crept northward toward the Mediterranean coast in North Africa where Carthage once flourished; today, the fingers of the Sahara are also reaching southward into Central Africa.

Some deserts, if their soil has the proper texture and nutrient values, can support agriculture with irrigation. But the cost of importing water may make the cost of producing crops prohibitively high, and also the attrition of water through evaporation creates a danger of large deposits of salts in the soil which will make it too toxic for plants. Historians still aren't sure what terminated man's earliest civilizations, but toxic soil is the most likely and logical reason—among the dusty ruins in the desert wastes between the Tigris and Euphrates rivers are the remains of elaborate irrigation networks.

The high rate of evaporation characterizes a desert as much as or more than the low input of moisture. The desert is an excellent natural laboratory in which to study how survival is accomplished under environmental duress. Even with hard competition for water, organisms can achieve maturity and health; there simply are fewer individuals and they are widely spaced.

Plants employ different strategies to acquire and conserve water. The cactus and other succulents have numerous cavities and widespread shallow root systems to soak up maximum amounts of water during the rainy season, storing the precious fluid for gradual year-long consumption. Mesquite roots, on the other hand, have penetrated as deep as 175 feet to tap ground water. The creosote bush, a dominant plant of the hot desert in southwestern United States, has evergreen leaves that are heavily waxed and resistant to the drying effects of air and sunlight. Some plants curl their leaves by day to reduce the exposed area and cut transpiration. Other plants survive the long, dry summers by shedding their leaves, the equivalent of other vegetation's reaction to winter. The annuals exist through dry periods as seeds coated with a growth-inhibitor that is washed away only by the first substantial rain. The debut of the rainy season activates dormant insect eggs and pupae so that the flowering desert swarms with crickets, grasshoppers, ants, bees, wasps, butterflies, moths, and beetles.

The kangaroo rat estivates (hibernates during the summer) through the dry season. This rodent, like the gerbils of the Middle East and Africa, can live without drinking water, obtaining moisture from its own metabolic processes. It has no sweat glands and, like most desert mammals, remains underground during the day. The camel sweats, but not until its body temperature reaches about 105 degrees. The animal's fat is stored in its hump instead of all over its body where it would impede the outward flow of interior heat while its thick coat shields the body against the broiling exterior—all contributing to conservation of water.

Still, most of this information concerns only the ecological area of the organism's adjustment to its environment. Not as much is known about how the desert ecosystem works, its rate of mineral turnover or cycling, the interrelationships of its organisms, or how the creatures which live there affect the desert.

4

More is known about the other biome existing under extreme climatic pressure—the tundra—and the knowledge stocked the arsenal for the battle for the Alaskan wilderness.

It is fair to say that tundra is the ecosystem operating closest to the perimeter of survival. It is the least productive of all types of terrestrial biomes and has the lowest metabolism. (Desert, on the other hand, is quite productive, but has a high metabolism and therefore supports the smallest accumulated biomass.) Like the desert, tundra does not receive much water, but unlike desert its evaporation rate is very low so that lack of moisture is not a problem. The limiting factors are severe cold and a shortage of radiant energy. As a result, tundra is only minimally productive, and also supports relatively few species of organisms. Nevertheless, it is a stable ecosystem, showing remarkable tenacity in its confrontation with adversity. But its equilibrium is of a low order: it is easily disturbed and recovers very slowly.

The tundra essentially is an arctic grassland, a frozen plain encircling the top of the world. It is clothed in lichen, grasses, sedges, dwarf woody plants; dotted with lakes and laced with streams, and for most of the year gelid from the surface to a depth of 1,200 feet. This is permafrost. In the summer when the sun rarely leaves the sky, the veneer thaws into a quagmire; there is little drainage for the freed water.

The resident organisms seize upon the abbreviated growing season to carry out accelerated life cycles. The ground squirrel mates almost as soon as it emerges from hibernation in May. The young are born in mid-June after 25 days of gestation, are self-sufficient by mid-July, and are fully matured adults ready to hibernate by late September. The northern robin feeds its young for 21 hours each long summer day and the chicks are able to leave the nest after eight days, compared to about two weeks in the continental United States.

The general circumscription of life is seen in the limitation of species, the paucity of alternative food sources, and reflected in short food chains: lichen→caribou (or reindeer in Eurasia)→man/wolf, or: grass→lemming→arctic fox/snowy owl. It is also manifested in sharp oscillations of animal populations. Every three or four years, the lemming population undergoes a build-up, reaches a peak, consumes inordinate amounts of grass, crashes before the vegetation is permanently injured, then starts to build once again. The famous lemming migrations take place only during years when the population attains extraordinary concentrations. The cycle of the arctic fox follows that of its lemming prey. When the lemmings die off, the fall of the fox population is not far behind. The snowy owl also virtually disappears after the lemming collapse, but the owls are able to avoid the fate of lemmings and foxes by emigrating. Every three or four years, American ornithologists as far south as North Carolina expect to see a few more snowy owls.

The rate of decay in tundra is slow because decomposer bacteria are hampered by the low temperatures. The rate of plant growth is slow not only because of the adverse temperatures and short season, but also apparently because nutrients cannot be recycled well through the sluggish ecosystem. This is what makes tundra peculiarly vulnerable: nature's incapacity to heal its wounds.

The migration of caribou is a mechanism to circumvent the slow growth rate of vegetation. The herds move to new pastures before destroying the resource upon which they depend. In fact this is the reason that migration is common to grazing herds throughout the world. It is curious that land destruction through overgrazing has been caused over the centuries not by animal populations but by shepherds and ranchers—members of the species that distinguishes itself from all others by its intelligence.

If some obstacle suddenly intercepted the caribou herds, constricting their range, overgrazing might then become unavoidable. The caribou would become the *Acanthaster planci* of Alaska, metamorphosed into marauders of their own habitat and catalysts to their own doom. This is what is happening when African elephants take refuge in sanctuaries not sufficiently large to support them. The future of both habitat and animal is in doubt. For when the home goes, so do its inhabitants. When a forest is leveled, the animal and bird species in it are extinguished. It is like the sacking of a city.

So one of the dangers of an oil pipeline transecting Alaska from Prudhoe Bay on the Arctic Ocean to the warm water port of Valdez is that it could cause caribou to degrade or denude remote areas of Alaskan landscape and even eliminate the caribou, upon which some Eskimos depend.

Installing the 800-mile Trans-Alaska Pipeline System would be like branding the ecosystem with a red-hot poker. The oil gushes out of the North Slope at a temperature of 160 degrees, a scalding 200 degrees hotter than the tundra surface in winter. If the 4-foot pipeline rested directly on the tundra, not only would the permafrost melt but sections of the pipe might shift or sag in the mush, and hemorrhage. The escaping oil would have no place to go, no ocean in which to disperse. No one knows how long the incubus would afflict the prostrate natural ecosystem. But we have a hint.

An earlier exploration for oil was conducted across 23 million acres east of Prudhoe Bay at the end of World War Two. Twenty-five years later the bulldozers' ruts and gouges abide, indelible in the arctic matrix. The natural deep freeze has preserved a junkyard of shacks, oil drums, and garbage.

A lake of oil would have a similar opportunity for longevity.

5

Fortunately, other ecosystems are more resilient. Even so, the decrease in natural productivity in the mainland United States is substantial, and measurable—from the eroded soil and degraded vegetation of the West to the decimation of valuable fisheries in Lake Erie to the dwindling biomass of the eastern deciduous forest.

This forest makes a good comparison with the tundra and desert, for the eastern hardwoods have been comparatively well studied and the forest is probably the most successful of all terrestrial ecosystems from the standpoint of survival. (Trees themselves are superior organisms because they live longer—bristlecone pine, 4,500 or more years—and grow larger—redwoods, 370 feet—than any other living thing. Adult sequoias are virtually fire and disease-proof.)

Immediately one is aware of the difference in profiles of the low-order systems with that of the forest. Nearly half of the desert's total organic matter is in roots—a defense against aridity. Most of the remaining desert material is in the form of litter—dead leaves, needles, twigs, and so forth. More than 90 percent of the desert biomass is made up of roots and litter. Only one percent exists as year-round material such as branches. The rest is green parts and leaves. In tundra, three quarters of the biomass is in roots and rhizomes, the underground stems, where the organisms are better protected against cold.

In the deciduous forest, three-quarters of the organic matter is in trunks and branches and most of the rest in roots. Ninety-seven percent of the forest biomass exists in perennial plant material. The forest biomass is more than 13 times as great as that of tundra and 20 times as great as the organic matter the desert can support. Unlike the other two ecosystems, the forest rises into the sky, millions of individuals vying for the life-giving light.

The forest profile above ground has four layers. The top layer in this stratification is the upper canopy consisting of the dominant trees of the forest. The lower canopy is formed by secondary trees. Then come the shrubs and young trees and finally the ground layer with seedlings, herbs, ferns, and mosses. Mammals live mostly at the ground level (in tropical rain forests most mammals live in the tree canopies). As for birds, scarlet tanagers dwell in the upper canopy, red-eyed vireos inhabit the lower canopy, while woodpeckers and nuthatches live in the open spaces of tree trunks. Investigators have found that each of these kinds of birds spends almost all its time in one stratum. (It quite literally knows its own level, although this behavior does not have the social connotation it does for human class strata.)

In the tree population, however, the species that finds or makes room at the top most influences the composition of the entire community (a pine forest, for instance, produces a much more acidic and leached soil and, because of year-round shade, a less well-developed understory). For with moderate temperatures and adequate moisture, light is the controlling environmental factor. If the desert ecosystem is characterized by a struggle for water, the forest is distinguished by competition for light. Deciduous forests that have mature trees all of the same age and height because of logging or fire have uniformly dense canopies, casting more shade than odd-age stands and, like the conifers, have poorly developed undergrowth.

In an oak or maple forest only about six percent of the midday summer sunlight reaches the forest floor whereas about 65 percent of the rain gets through. Summer is the darkest period of the year for the plants at ground level. Because of shedding of leaves, and changing length of daylight, there is enormous seasonal fluctuation of light. The forest floor gets its most light in March and April with a second, lower peak in the fall. In response to this bath of light, the deciduous forest has much more fully developed lower strata than conifers, and a procession of different plants through the seasons.

Ecologists have made painstaking studies of the forest ecosystem to find out how it works and why. For example, John Cantlon wanted to know exactly how vegetation differed on the north and south slopes of Cushetunk Mountain in New Jersey. So he took a census. He found that 21,987 trees grew in an area of 3,500 square meters on the south slope whereas only 15,759 trees grew on a north slope area of the same size. On the south slope there were most dogwood trees followed by ash, sassafras, and tulip, while on the north slope the sequence was ash, witch hazel, birch, and maple. The maple was fourteenth in abundance on the south slope, the birch ninth, and the witch hazel did not grow tall enough to reach into the tree canopy.

This is how the various tree populations responded to the sharply different environmental conditions of the two slopes. These local variations, because of different elevations, streams, north or south slopes—forming what ecologists call microclimates—occur throughout the forest biome. And so there is great variety in the deciduous forest.

Generally, however, the entire biome has just a few major subdivisions where certain species of trees have the largest populations. The forests are named for these dominants because they figure so importantly in that particular type of forest. There is the beech-sugar maple forest of the north central region, the maple-basswood forest of Wisconsin and Minnesota, the oak-hickory forest of the western and southern regions, the mixed forest of the Appalachian plateau, and the pine forest of the southeast.

6

It is not a matter of chance that these characteristic forest communities appear over wide areas. They are the product of prolonged sorting of species by immigration and extinction until there is a fine adjustment to the constraints of the physical environment. These final, very stable communities are arrived at by a process known as ecological succession.

The surface of a boulder hardly seems an hospitable place for life, yet it can begin there. For one thing, the rock is exposed to disintegrative processes of weathering. Falling rain absorbs carbon dioxide from the air to form a mild carbonic acid. Over the years, this acid dissolves some of the more soluable minerals from the boulder, leaving crevices where water may enter. In winter, the water freezes and expands, widening the fractures. In summer, the glare of sun causes the rock surface to expand: new fissures are opened. Gradually, the boulder breaks and begins to disintegrate; the fine particles are some of the stuff that soil is made of.

Lichen has the ability to gain a foothold on the boulder surface and contribute to the soil-making process. In primary plant succession, lichens are the pioneers. Lichen actually is two plants—an alga and a fungus—living together in a symbiosis that benefits both. The alga uses its chlorophyll to make food for itself and the colorless fungus while the fungus secretes acids that dissolve the rock to expose life-giving nutrients. The fungus also provides a water-absorbent tissue for catching rain on the rock's dry surface.

Once it has established an outpost, the lichen contributes to rock disintegration and to soil building. Bits of rock particles, wind-blown dust, and scraps of organic matter are tucked away in crannies. With accumulation of this material, with the lichens storing moisture, the environment becomes suitable for less hardy plants—a seedbed for mosses and ferns, then annual weeds. The process accelerates: more plants, more organic matter, more soil, more water, until herbs and shrubs are able to colonize the area. Their roots put further pressure on the substratum rock, widening the crevices. Root secretions enhance the weathering process. The rock crumbles further. At the same time more plant litter contributes to a growing layer of humus. Animals begin to use the area; their droppings add new materials.

The buildup of soil goes on until, finally, a tree seedling takes root. One day what once was a bare boulder will be another part of the forest.

This start from scratch is known as primary succession. What is perhaps more common in the eastern United States is secondary succession—what happens to cropland or pastures, fields or gardens, when they are left unattended. In this case the soil already is formed. And this is an important advantage, for soil is the crossroads between the organic and mineral worlds, and an ecosystem in its own right with producers, herbivores, and predators ... although largely dependent upon the plants that take root. To indicate how extensively and how incredibly fast plants exploit the substrate, one study showed that in four months, a plant of winter rye grass grew a root system that included 378 miles of roots and some 6,000 miles of root hairs—a daily average growth of three miles of roots and 50 miles of root hairs.

Except for the essential mineral nutrients that plants draw from the earth, soil mainly acts as a firm yet malleable medium in which plants can anchor themselves and as a reservoir for water. Indeed, hydroponics, the art of growing plants outside of soil, is a tangible demonstration of this principle. In hydroponics, the plants are grown in nutrient cultures—either water or sand or gravel—with the necessary nutrients supplied. G.I.s were fed from hydroponic gardens on Ascension Island in the mid-Atlantic Ocean during the Second World War and the U.S. Army initiated two extensive hydroponic farms in Japan after the war. The main advantage of hydroponics is that high yields can be attained in areas where soils are toxic or infertile. However, the artificial process is expensive and is economically feasible only where highly desired crops are otherwise unobtainable.

When the plant dies, the roots as well as its above-surface material become food for the myriad creatures inhabiting the soil (fallen leaves, animal droppings, and dead animals are other items on the menu). Microbial organisms—bacteria, fungi, protozoa—begin breaking down the dead organic matter. Some nematodes join in the repast. Earthworms, pot worms, millipedes, and small soil arthropods take in and process enormous amounts of organic matter of which they actually use only small amounts. One researcher estimates that up to 36 tons of organic matter and soil pass through the alimentary tracts of earthworms living in one acre. In this way the soil is turned over and given a spongy character. Feeding on the pot worms and nematodes are the predators of the next trophic level—mites, insects, and spiders.

Perhaps the most impressive part of the soil equation is the size of its populations—four and a half billion organisms, nearly three tons of bacteria alone, can share an acre. In time, the bodies of the minute animals themselves become part of the soil. Through decomposition, the organic debris of the forest is turned into humus, a sort of way station for organic material on its route back to such inorganic products as water, carbon dioxide, minerals, and salts. In this way humus enriches soil, making available to plants vital nutrients and water.

Soil, then, is a mix of parent geologic material, organic matter, air, and water. A cut-away profile of soil shows a series of layers, or horizons as they are called, from the litter of leaves on top through various stages of decomposed humus to an area without nutrients to a stratum of mineralized organic matter mixed with finely divided parent material to the underlying ground layer. The layer without minerals exists because calcium, potassium, sodium, and other nutrients have been leached out of the soil by rain water percolating down to the ground water. Most of the nutrients are recycled back into new plants, but a certain percentage of the minerals keeps moving in a general exodus to the sea.

The texture and porosity of soil determine how quickly water moves through. Soil particles are classified from gravel (particles larger than two millimeters), sand, silt, to clay (particles too fine to be seen under an ordinary microscope). Sandy soils may retain from 10 to 15 percent of their weight in water, clay 50 to 70 percent. Humus can hold up to 200 percent of its weight in water.

Forest soil with humus four inches deep may store more than one and a half inches of rainwater, distributing this moisture gradually for several days after a rain. In this way, very little of the valuable moisture is lost in run-off to streams, or at least not before it has served the forest ecosystem. For man, this means that water supplies are lowered, but are more evenly distributed than in the flood-drought system of barren countryside. Reforestation has been proposed for centuries to protect the cultural treasures of Florence, Italy, from floods, but while Italians and people from many other nations are willing to make great sacrifices to reclaim the art work ravaged by flood waters this natural insurance policy is not instituted.

In forests, litter and roots decay slowly, but mineralization is rapid. The result is a relatively narrow layer of humus. In grassland, not only is the process reversed—rapid humification, slow mineralization—but the whole grass plant dies, so that there is a great production of humus.

So we can see why the black, humus-laden chernozem soil of the eastern prairie that supported the tall grass became the agricultural breadbasket of the United States, and why grasslands, in general, with proper rainfall are the granaries of the world. The average humus content of grass-land soil is 600 tons per acre compared to about 50 tons an acre for forest soil. Infertile soils may have only 10 or 15 tons.

When one considers that it may take as long as 500 years to build an inch of topsoil—as long as 20,000 years for well-developed soils to achieve an equilibrium with mineral weathering and erosion—then one can appreciate the magnitude of the loss in fertility when, each year, two billion tons of sediment are washed away from American farmlands by rains and irrigation.

In secondary succession with soil already formed, the progression of plant communities moves along more quickly. The hardy pioneers, in this case, are annuals, what everyone knows as "weeds." So the year after farmer Jones abandons his corn field, the next production is a crop of weeds, the prime invaders of disturbed land. These plants have short life cycles; their seeds are highly mobile and can remain dormant for long periods until they reach a favorable environment. They can prosper in substrate low in nutrients and organic matter, are drought-tolerant, can grow in bright sunlight, and withstand wide variations in temperature. The combinations of early colonizers are immense, depending upon location, climate, soil conditions, and chance. On Long Island, about 100 to 150 herbaceous species take part in the first five or six years of colonization of abandoned land. The first year, the pigweed, which grows to a height of more than three feet, is abundant. During the second year, horseweed is conspicuous. Crabgrass is common. In subsequent years, grasses such as broomsedge and asters become dominants.

After three or four years, these plants have modified the environment to such an extent that perennial grasses gain supremacy. Their longer life cycles—earlier growth in spring, later growth in summer—put the pioneers at a disadvantage. Other natives follow. With further change, the field becomes suitable for more demanding plants, ones that require moderate temperatures, richer soil, some shade from the sunlight in order to grow. Shrubs move in. As the larger woody plants reach maturity they overshadow their predecessors. For a while the species may coexist, but after ten or fifteen years, twenty at most, the grasses are eliminated. In the meantime, seedlings of pine, elm, aspen, burr oak, and red maple have taken root.

After about twenty-five years, a young forest is taking form, with pine the dominant tree. But their shade interferes with the growth of their young trees. Beech, sugar maple, and hemlock, however, can thrive in the dark understory. And these, growing taller year by year, finally come to dominate the forest.

This is the climax to the succession of plant communities. The beech-maple climax or the other climax communities have now come into an equilibrium with the environment that allows them to perpetuate the community without further change. It takes a century or more, perhaps 150 years for the beech-maple climax to achieve ascendancy and perhaps two centuries for this deciduous forest to mature completely from an old field. On bare sand dunes and lava beds arrival at a climax forest through primary succession may take a millennium.

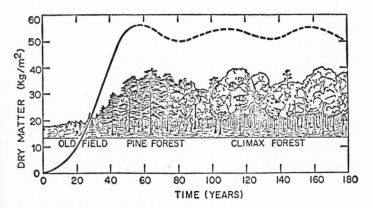

FOREST GROWTH CURVE
(The Oscillations of Climax Are Assumed)
—from *Radiation and the Patterns of Nature*
by George M. Woodwell

The final stability achieved by the climax is not a steady-state affair, but a dynamic equilibrium that adjusts as requirements warrant. Through the analysis of layers of pollen and with radiocarbon dating, Paul Sears discerned a chronology of adjustments made by the mature forest in northern Ohio to broad climatic changes following the recession of the most recent glacier about 12,000 years ago. During the early cool moist period, the forest was dominated by spruce and firs, but shifted to pines with some oaks as the climate warmed and dried about 7000 B.C. As the climate became more humid, beeches gained ascendancy and so on until the present when maples with hemlocks and pines are most prolific.

The species of animals change with the various plant communities of succession. Among birds, for example, the sparrows and meadowlarks live in the early grass field while thrushes, warblers, and woodpeckers do not arrive until establishment of the hardwood forest a century later. Most game birds thrive in what are early, and temporary, communities.

According to the law of succession, this progression *always* occurs, everywhere, in all forest ecosystems.

A similar pattern holds for grassland. A study of abandoned wagon roads used by American pioneers across the prairie showed that the bare ground ruts first were invaded by the weeds and annuals. The weed stage lasted from two to five years, giving way to short-lived grasses. They first appeared in the third year and lasted until the tenth. The third stage, early perennial grass, occupied the second decade. The climax grass stage was achieved in twenty to forty years.

In edge country at the boundary between climax forest and climax grassland, there may be an incessant border war. In wet years the trees set up outposts in the grassland only to have the grasses rally and reconsolidate during the dry years.

7

Ecosystem aging takes place in lakes, with a different kind of meaning for mankind.

When lakes are first formed—the Great Lakes and many others in North America were left by the retreating glaciers —they are devoid of life. Young lakes are clear and a deep blue since there is nothing to reflect the shorter wave-lengths. Sapphire-pure Lake Tahoe on the California-Nevada border maintained an exceptional ecological youth because of its fortunate location in a low-nutrient forest watershed, extreme depth (1,650 feet) and great volume, excellent drainage, and isolation. The lake lost the last advantage with the arrival of a tourist industry in recent years and now is growing old before its time.

A young lake is known ecologically as oligotrophic—for sparse feedings. The spearheads of the lake invasion are plankton, microscopic algae, and animals. Gradually nutrients enter the lake from the surrounding watershed, the plankton multiply and upon death settle to the bottom to form a layer of muck. The ooze creates a substrate for water weeds and rooted green alga plants. These plants bind the bottom sediments into a firmer layer and add to the organic material in the lake.

The lake becomes more eutrophic—that is, good feeding —and invites more, and different, species of organisms. Small caddisflies arrive to feed on the benthic microorganisms. Trout, lake herring, whitefish—some of man's most prized fish delicacies—live in oligotrophic lakes. As the process toward eutrophy goes on, diatoms replace desmids as the dominant phytoplankton, to be followed by flagellates and other green algae. These all are species that apparently are desired by crustaceans and other small aquatic animals who themselves make tasty provender for larger fish. Along with the crustaceans, dragonflies and mayflies appear. The early fish community yields to a new society of bass, perch, and pike.

The addition of more organic matter begins to reduce the water depth and provides nutrients for floating plants that embed their roots into the bottom muck, spreading their leaves to float on the water's surface. After the floating plants come frogs, diving beetles, and insects that can live on the underside of the floating plants.

While the phytoplankton and plants supply oxygen to the lake, the other organisms—particularly in the decomposition of the organic matter—are consuming oxygen, reducing the dissolved oxygen in the water. The bass, perch, and pike give way to the hardier but less favored carp or sunfish. Since water pollution in many cases is simply the overloading of nutrients, sanitation officials can judge the degree of pollution by examining the aquatic community.

As the edge of the lake grows more shallow, it becomes exposed to air during seasonal fluctuations. The floating plants cannot survive the changed environment and they yield to emergent plants—cattail sedges, bulrushes, and arrowheads firmly anchored into the bottom. Ducks and muskrats are seen. Blue-green algae become the dominant phytoplankton and begin to give the water a pea-soup consistency. Blue-greens are dead ends instead of bases for the food pyramid. Zooplankton and most other organisms won't eat blue-green algae. Consequently, they become overabundant and their noxious blooms are notorious in degraded waters. A few consecutive dark days with insufficient energy radiation to sustain the algal masses will cause a massive die-off and the rotting matter further depletes the oxygen.

In the impoverished environment, bullheads have supplanted sunfish and annelid worms have colonized the bottom muck. Because of the emergent plants, the substrate builds up rapidly with great deposits of organic matter. Most of the open water is covered with sedges, cattails and their tribe of plants, and the lake or pond gets a new name. It is a marsh.

And still the transformation proceeds. With continual addition of organic matter, the bottom rises above ground water level and dries in the summer. The marsh becomes a temporary pond that supports only the organisms that can withstand drying in summer and freezing in winter. As the land rises still more, the emergent plants no longer can survive. The land, now completely above the water level, is invaded by meadow grasses and land animals. It is now a marsh meadow.

Lakes naturally grow old and die very slowly. No one knows the natural lifetime of a lake, but for a large lake it is many thousands of years. Longevity is associated with size, watershed, drainage, and perhaps factors still unknown. The man-caused acceleration of aging is called cultural eutrophication. Limnologist Arthur Hasler estimates that one-third of the 100,000 lakes in the United States are endangered by this eutrophication.

No one knows how long the Great Lakes, if left alone, would exist before they became senile. But the small lake whose life history was telescoped here will proceed rather rapidly, in a few short centuries, to become a forest if it resides in the eastern biome.

That is the law of succession. And while it turns a lake into a meadow, it also transforms a bare field into a forest which is a reservoir for water. Not only does the humus husband water, but there is less than one-half the moisture evaporation in a forest than in an open field. The forest has created a new environment, a shield against the harsh sunlight, intense heat, erosive wind; it has contrived ways to conserve water, tap the earth for minerals and become a depot as well for the nutrients; it has converted the land from hard-packed, inhospitable earth or impervious rock into porous soil teeming with life.

In this way, the forest has survived for a quarter of a billion years. Not as one tree. Not as a few talented or outstanding or brave individuals. Nor as a handful of lovable egocentrics. As an ecosystem, a whole system.

When blight in this century eliminated the chestnut tree, one of the major dominants of the deciduous biome, the assault did not bring down the hardwood forests of the East. The system adjusted, and rather quickly, to the change. A year-long drought would be severe hardship to a farmer, probably ruin his crops. The same drought produces no noticable effect upon the mature forest. During the protracted Midwestern drought of the 1930s the mature grassland managed to survive and to hold down the soil. The grassland that had been cultivated for crops or overgrazed suffered complete biological collapse followed by wind erosion, creating what was called the Dust Bowl in that period.

Ecologists have devoted much thought to the meaning of succession and the climax community. The scientists have observed that not only do the plant species change in an orderly progression, but each stage modifies the environment in such a way that it gives an advantage to the succeeding community. The beginning is elementary. The pioneer stage of crabgrass and weeds can shelter no large animals and is attractive to few birds. The plant species are few. The number of species of plants and animals increases as the ecosystem grows toward maturity.

This development is accompanied by a growth in productivity and biomass. Starting gradually at first, then accelerating through the shrub and pine forest stages, the rate of production far exceeds respiration. This production, of course, becomes the growing bulk of the forest. In general this growth in biomass follows the same S-curve that applies to the growth of an individual, a human, for instance. The infant starts slowly, then shoots up through late childhood and teens, to level off in adulthood.

As the ecosystem reaches maturity, the net production tapers off, the forest unit stops growing in biomass, and the system comes into a metabolic balance. Productivity tends to match total respiration. The photosynthetic production goes to maintain the ecosystem which has reached the maximum size compatible to the climate and resources of the area.

But something else has been happening. Not only has the forest been growing in size, it has been growing in complexity, a ramification that goes on well after the ecosystem achieves its maximum productivity. The diversity of species has been increasing. Instead of a few producers with a narrow range of light fixation, there are many with overlapping capabilities. Simple food chains become complex food webs. If one predator succumbs to some environmental change, several others move in to hold a fast-multiplying insect species in check. As the ecosystem becomes more complex structurally, it does so functionally as well: there are more rôles for different species to fill, more opportunities to exploit the resources, more ways to utilize the energy, more repositories for the photosynthetic products, more storehouses for minerals, more collectors of moisture and containers of water, more routes for the nutrients, more alternatives and options, more self-correcting feedbacks to maintain balanced flow and populations.

Professor Odum suggests that maximum production cannot be the ultimate goal of the ecosystem. He notes that trees keep adding leaves when the system has reached productive capacity. So the extra leaves must be for some other purpose. He reminds that the kinds and number of species, the structure and metabolism of the ecosystem undergo elaboration after maximum production. And he concludes that stability itself "may well be the primary purpose (that is, the survival value) of ecological succession when viewed from the evolutionary standpoint."

That was written in Professor Odum's book, *Ecology*, in 1963. Six years later in the paper "The Strategy of Ecosystem Development," Dr. Odum goes on to say, "the 'strategy' of succession as a short-term process is basically the same as the 'strategy' of long-term evolutionary development of the biosphere—namely, increased control of . . . the physical environment in the sense of achieving maximum protection from its perturbations."

In other words, the goal of the biological community is to achieve both stability within its physical setting and maximum ability to adjust to whatever changes may take place. "The overall strategy is, as I stated at the beginning of this article," Dr. Odum goes on, "directed toward achieving as large and diverse an organic structure as is possible within the limits set by the available energy input and the prevailing physical conditions of existence (soil, water, climate, and so on)."

"The climax community results when no other combination of species is successful in outcompeting or replacing the climax community," states Edward Kormondy in *Concepts of Ecology*. "But," says Dr. Kormondy, "stability of the climax is certainly not so simply explained. The answer lies in an as yet not fully understood property—diversity."

"In other words," says Dr. Odum, "is variety only the spice of life, or is it a necessity for the long life of the total ecosystem comprising man and nature?"

CHAPTER FOUR

The Diverse System

1

ABOUT SIX MONTHS after the encounter of the Pacific task force with the crown-of-thorns starfish, two scientists from the Smithsonian Institution discovered that *Acanthaster planci* has a second predator. Ecologist Lee Talbot and his wife Martha, a biologist, attending a scientific meeting in Tanzania, seized at the passing reference to a capability of the painted shrimp, *Hymenocera elegans*, to feed on crown-of-thorns. Later the Talbots saw a demonstration at the Max Planck Institute for Behavioral Physiology in Munich.

Indeed, *H. elegans* can demolish *A. planci*, 10 times bigger and 100 times heavier than *H. elegans* which is, after all, a shrimp. But it is a shrimp immune to the crown-of-thorns' poison. For its opening gambit, the russet and white crustacean lifts one of the starfish's arms and tickles some of the tube feet, which are immediately retracted. With this wedge, *elegans* proceeds to overturn the giant, flipping the sea star onto its back. In phase three, the painted shrimp methodically tamps down the rest of the tube feet until all are withdrawn.

Now the crustacean has the entire soft underside of the immobilized starfish at its disposal. With a scalpel-sharp pincer, the shrimp punctures the flesh and tears out chunks of meat, the beginning of a feast upon the strangely helpless nemesis of the coral reef.

While it takes *A. planci*'s customary predator, triton, one week to consume a starfish, shrimp can turn a crown-of-thorns into a mass of jelly in one day. And while painted shrimp are not native to the coral reefs, they are known to survive there. So scientists envision the possibility of containing the *A. planci* plague naturally. But they are cautious about introducing an armada of shrimp into an exotic environment to conquer sea stars, a novel caution that indicates the growing influence of ecology. Among many facts ecologists want to know is—whether, if this biological control is successful, scientists next year will have to conduct a frenzied search for the predator of *Hymenocera elegans* and so on, *ad infinitum*? Or, what *else* does the painted shrimp eat?

"The practical implication of an ecological system," says biologist Garrett Hardin, "is just this: we can never do merely one thing." Were they alive today, those Hawaiian plantation owners who welcomed the mongoose might second the thought.

In contrast to that mongoose experiment, the U.S. Air Force became involved in an enterprise based on more thorough ecological knowledge. In the fall of 1967, the Air Force had a bizarre traffic problem. The joint U.S.-Spanish airbase at Torejón near Madrid was bedeviled by flocks of a wild game bird, the bustard. Jet fighter pilots taking off and landing at the base had to fly the gauntlet of stork-like bustards dodging into their flight path. There were enough jet-bustard collisions to inflict one-and-a-half million dollars worth of damage to Air Force hardware in 1967. Still, the battered bustards of Torejón refused to get out of the way.

The Air Force tried to evict the undesirables with conventional weapons—rifle fire—without success. An escalation to grenades and chemical warfare—poisons—was considered and rejected because of possible harm to other wildlife.

Essentially, the problem was that bustards did not know how powerful man is and did not fear him. Finally the Air Force appealed to naturalist Felix de la Fuente, who knew an answer to their problem. Sr. de la Fuente trapped six peregrine falcons and trained them to hunt on command, a practice that goes back into prehistory but fell into disuse with the advent of rifles, grenades, and jet fighters.

Not only were de la Fuente's falcons effective as hunters, but the bustards recognized their natural enemy and fled from the scene. Where more than 10,000 bustards had been sighted in 1967, there were virtually none left two years later.

What turned out to be a classic illustration of predator-prey relationships grew out of the conservation fervor President Theodore Roosevelt brought to the White House at the turn of the century. At that time, the deer population in the United States was at a low ebb. The white-tailed deer in the East had been virtually eliminated by hunting for sport and venison.

In 1907, the government decided to protect a herd of 4,000 deer on Kaibab Plateau, an area of about 725,000 acres on the north side of Grand Canyon in Arizona. A bounty was placed on the predators of the deer—cougars, wolves, and coyotes.

The campaign went well. Six hundred mountain lions were liquidated in the first ten years. Destruction of the other predatory species kept pace. The result was a dramatic affirmation of the cause-effect relationship of predation. The deer population ballooned tenfold, by 1918 numbering 40,000. But, naturally, something else was happening.

There were signs of overbrowsing. Some investigators recommended a moratorium on the predator program, but the recommendations went unheeded.

In 1920, there was the first report of a fawn dying of starvation. Still there was no let-up in the extermination format. Seventy-four more pumas were killed between 1918 and 1923. Three thousand coyotes were slain between 1907 and 1923. During that same period, 11 wolves were killed; 19 more by 1926 when the last wolf was gone. But with a friend like man the deer didn't need enemies.

The Kaibab herd reached 100,000 deer in 1924. Sixty thousand of them died of starvation and disease during the next two winters. The deer had eaten everything within reach—grasses, trees, seedlings, shrubs. The range was so degraded that the deer population kept sliding. By 1929, the herd numbered 30,000. By 1931, 20,000. By 1939, the deer population leveled off at 10,000. With unflagging determination to help the deer, rangers and bounty hunters kept slaughtering the remaining predators—poisoning or otherwise dispatching 4,388 coyotes, 142 more cougars. The U.S. Department of the Interior and the State of Arizona have not yet caught up with early 20th-century ecology—they *still* conduct a systematic program of predator extermination in the state.

Naturalist-author Edward Abbey tells of a current lion "control" program being conducted by the Interior Department's Bureau of Sport Fisheries and Wildlife on Music Mountain. Abbey quotes the bureau's state supervisor Robert Shiver as saying it is an experimental program started because hunters want more deer and fewer lions. Abbey asked what experimental meant. "We want to see what effect the program will have on the deer population," Shiver replied.

Of all the interactions among populations, the predator-prey relationship undoubtedly is the one that most fascinates man. The reason may be because he is the non-pareil predator. Which could also explain why he behaves with such hostility toward other animal predators and sometimes sympathizes with their prey, although (as in the case of the Kaibab deer) his kindness can be devastating.

Ecologists are concerned with the predator-prey relationship because not only is it one of the important transfer links as energy passes through the food web, but it is one of the common actions at the interface of species. But, ecologically, predation is only one sector of interspecific interaction. The David-Goliath contest of the painted shrimp and crown-of-thorns is unorthodox in that the predator usually is superior to its prey in size and strength. Snakes and spiders which subdue their prey with poison or fear are also exceptions to this rule.

Generally, when a small organism lives off a large one, it is a parasite-host relationship. Various guides are given to distinguish predation from parasitism. That matter of size is one: if the attacking organism is larger, it is a predator. Parasitism is a case of the weak attacking the strong. Ecologist Elton has said that predators live on capital while parasites live on interest.

The longer the relationship has been in existence, the more reconciled the two populations become to the interaction with a consequent reduction in the disturbance. The cowbird and European cuckoos have become so parasitic that they have lost the ability to build nests, incubate eggs, and care for their young. They, of course, deposit their eggs in the nests of other birds, the cuckoo being so masterful at this that it can imitate the eggs of the host. In defense, most of the birds either throw out the alien egg, build another nest over it, or rear their own young successfully along with the uninvited guests. But when the cowbird was introduced to the Kirtland's warbler as a result of forest clearing, the warbler population was seriously affected. The warbler had learned no defense against the intrusion, and since the cowbird chicks hatched earlier, they exploited a competitive advantage to the detriment of young warblers.

Even though efficient parasites do not kill their hosts, the hosts frequently can become so debilitated that they are susceptible to other terminal disease. The lifespan of sufferers from schistosomiasis is notably shortened. This parasitic disease is caused by a worm that spends part of its cycle in the body of a snail and the rest in human organs. Similarly, malaria is caused by a parasite that travels from bloodstreams of human hosts via more than sixty species of *Anopheles* mosquities.

In addition to parasitic causes, disease can be produced by degenerative causes or nutritional failure, physiological stress, and, commonly, bacterial or viral infection. Ecologically, predation, parasitism, and disease all fulfill the same function in population control.

And the fascinating question of populations—how they remain stable despite exponential growth potential, how they remain stable despite severe environmental and competitive pressures, how the myriad plant and animal populations manage an astonishing degree of equilibrium in the community—is at the core of ecological inquiry.

2

A population is not a tangible organism that can be put into a garden or cage, but it is nevertheless an entity with its own unique characteristics, such as: birth rate, death rate, growth rate and form, age distribution, biotic potential, dispersion, and density.

Natality, the term used in ecology, is equivalent to birth rate, the term used in demography, the science of human population. Either term means, of course, the addition to the population through reproduction. Maximum or physiological natality is the birth potential or birth rate under ideal conditions. It is in this way that the awesome fecundity of many species is posed: the female codfish lays up to six million eggs per spawning; the termite queen 10,000 eggs per day, 500 million eggs in her lifetime; chickens 300 eggs a year; the record for a duck: 363 eggs in 365 days. The birth rate by itself is not necessarily the crucial factor.

Mortality, the death rate, is the statistical record of the number of individuals dying over a given time period or deaths as a percentage of the population. Anyone familiar with insurance actuarial tables knows about the death rate in a population. In the human population, particularly in civilization where modern medical practices, better nutrition, and other health improvements have extended longevity, a great number of individuals survive late into the lifespan and then there is a sharp drop-off. Oysters, on the other hand, lose most individuals near the beginning of life. Those that do survive the perilous beginning go on to live relatively long lives. In adult stages of many birds and mice, mortality rates are constant. Most animal populations have a high mortality rate early in life. Few populations, like the human one, embrace large numbers of individuals that live a good part of their lifespans.

Immigration into a population, like natality, increases its size while emigration away, like mortality, decreases its numbers. The interaction of these four plus and minus phenomena, over time, give each population its form.

There are two basic ways to describe this form, and they give a revealing picture of the state of a population, what is happening to it, what it is doing, where it is going. One representation is a population's age structure. For ecologists, the members of a population divide into three categories—prereproductive, reproductive, and postreproductive. If these categories are represented as percentages of the total population in the form of a pyramid, a rapidly expanding population would be very broad-based, showing the high percentage of young at the bottom. A declining population would have a relatively narrow base, tapering very gradually through the age groups. A population with a moderate number of young, characteristic of zero growth rate, would form a symmetrical pyramid between the first two extremes.

The very broad-based pyramids are typical of South America and Africa, continents with rapidly expanding populations. The base is not quite so broad for Asia. Europe typifies the narrow-based, low-growth population.

The United States has a relatively narrow middle be-

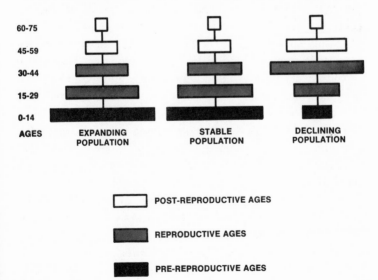

POPULATION PYRAMIDS

tween a wide base and a full top. To an ecologist, this means a minority of the population in the prime productive years is supporting a majority of unproductive population at either end of the age scale. The ecologist knows that if this trend toward larger unproductive segments continues, the imbalance must be corrected in some way. One way would be to expand the productive period—for example, postpone retirement until 70 years or 75 years. The way American society is maintaining the balance is by intensifying or expanding technology, so that each worker produces more. But if technology vitiates environment and environment ultimately governs population size, then something's got to give.

The prereproductive, reproductive, and postreproductive ages vary with species. In humans, the first stage (to age 15) comprises about 21 percent of the average lifetime, the second (from 15 to 45) about 42 percent, and the third postreproductive age, 37 percent. In the rat, these proportions are 25, 20, and 55 percent. On the other hand, the dragonfly spends two years in the egg and larval stages and is capable of reproduction for only one or two days during its four weeks of adulthood. Many birds and mammals have brief postreproductive ages. The story of the salmon's valiant hegira to spawn and die is well known.

The number of prereproductive females and the length of the reproductive age can tell ecologists a great deal about the future direction of a population. Two statistics are especially significant—the reproductive capacity, or maximum natality, per unit and the total number of units. One multiplied by the other gives the population's biotic potential, which tells how large any population can become under optimum circumstances. When an ecologist sees a bulging prereproductive group, he anticipates an accelerated growth rate. Growth rate, charted over a period of time, gives a population's growth curve.

The growth curve is a population's most important index. One line reveals a population's past and present, and may foretell its future.

R. H. MacArthur and J. H. Connell calculated that a bacterium, dividing every 20 minutes, at the end of 36 hours could produce an empire one foot deep over the entire earth. One hour later the mass would cover our heads. The power inherent in this exponential growth potential, according to biologist Hardin, is one concept that separates biologists from physicists who have no experience with such a force.

In reality, the bacteria's potential is never realized. Nevertheless, the only difference between bacteria and any other species is that the unicellular organism can multiply at a faster rate. *Every* species, as the Reverend Malthus warned, possesses the capacity to grow geometrically. The only difference is a minor adjustment in the time scale. Elephants are slow at reproduction. Even so, two elephants could be responsible for the reproduction of 17 million offspring, but the project would require 750 years.

If a few individuals of a species colonize a new area with favorable environmental conditions, the growth curve will start off slowly, then accelerate upwards in an ever more precipitous climb, giving ever fuller expression to biotic potential. If this skyrocketing population suddenly meets with a limiting factor—such as a first frost for annual plants or the harvesting of the crop upon which insects have been feeding—there is an abrupt plummeting of the growth curve. This represents a population crash. So the population curve looks like a J, and is characteristic of what happens to unchecked exponential growth. Investigators have found that the J growth curve is commonly associated with small organisms, such as plankton or insects, which have short life cycles, high biotic potential, high metabolism rate per gram, and relatively small biomass.

What the J curve indicates is a lack of governors on the population. The case of the Kaibab deer is an example even though the J still was relatively shallow when the population broke and the "crash" was not a plumbline to near-extinction.

Populations of most larger organisms follow a different course. The population starts out the same way—a slow growth that accelerates as the biotic potential takes hold. But then as the population reaches a certain relationship with its environment, the growth rate declines and the growth curve tapers into an S. This is the sigmoid growth

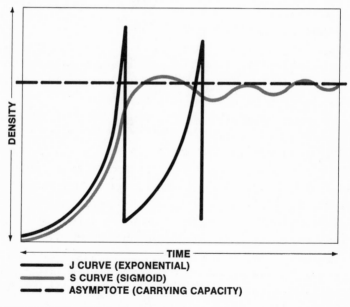

POPULATION GROWTH CURVES

curve, the form that represented the growth of the deciduous forest from an old field.

If the population achieves a perfect equilibrium with its environment, the growth rate drops to zero and the sigmoid ends with a straight horizontal line projecting from the top of the S along what is called the upper asymptote. This denotes that the population has reached its maximum size under existing conditions or the *carrying capacity* of that particular environment.

It is not uncommon for a population to overshoot this upper level. If the upper asymptote is exceeded by a slight amount, an adjustment occurs. Frequently, the adjustment brings the populations slightly under maximum capacity so that there is a subsequent readjustment upward, and so on, resulting in a mild oscillation of the growth curve along the upper asymptote. In the case of the Kaibab deer, the carrying capacity of the plateau turned out to be a population of 10,000 deer. As it happened, the deer population had exceeded the upper level by a factor of 10. Ecologists believe that originally the plateau had a carrying capacity of 30,000 deer, but this was cut two-thirds by the debasement of the range.

For some populations, violent oscillations are a way of life and must be regarded as a third characteristic form that the growth curve can take. These cyclic population swings occur frequently in marginal ecosystems where food chains are simplified with few checks or alternatives. Cyclic populations are common to many rodents and insects.

In a situation where a population has not reached its ultimate size and where the carrying capacity is unknown, it is impossible to predict with complete certainty what the shape of the growth curve will be. This is the case for the human population at the present moment in time. When ecologists meet this problem in connection with another species, they can make a very reliable estimate of the outcome by seeing how other populations of that species have performed under similar circumstances or consulting the growth patterns of similar species.

But because of the ability of *Homo sapiens* to manipulate his environment and produce his food, can the human situation be compared to that of other species? Not that the human growth curve looks any different from those of other species. The human population started to build gradually and now is rocketing upward. If you think of a sky writer in mid-letter, what we see now looks like the bottom half or more of a J. However, if human population growth levels off before the species surpasses its carrying capacity, then the figure turns into an S.

These two figures—S and J—portend two radically different fates. The S curve shows a population responsive to its environment, achieving equilibrium with its surroundings. The importance of being S is that members of this population can live in harmony with their surroundings and themselves. The J population—out of touch with or disregarding reality—is hurtling toward the throes of overcrowding, instability, famine, and high mortality.

Whatever the letter, there is an upper limit to the size of populations. The growth curve shows how a population is meeting its set of circumstances. The force that hammers the aspiring J into a responsible S is called environmental resistance, which stands for a whole inventory of limiting factors.

3

A German chemist named Justus Liebig proclaimed the principle of a limiting factor in the growth of plants. In 1840, Liebig enunciated this basic tenet of today's ecology:

"A beautiful connection subsists between the organic and inorganic kingdoms of nature. Inorganic matter affords food to plants, and they, on the other hand, yield the means of subsistence to animals."

The purpose of what he named organic chemistry, he said, "is to discover the chemical conditions essential to the life and perfect development of animals and vegetables." Thus was agriculture raised to a science, for Liebig investigated the mineral nutrients required by plants and discovered that when one of the nutrients was limited in supply, plant growth was curtailed. From this discovery, agriculture gained the use of fertilizers and ecology was bequeathed Liebig's "law of the minimum."

The concept of a limiting factor—which can be too much of something as well as too little—is one of the basic tools of the working ecologist. In one way or another he applies this rule when trying to learn why some organism is not present in a certain place or is present in abnormally low numbers. What is the limiting factor?

Three researchers—Nelson Hairston, Frederick Smith, and Lawrence Slobodkin—asked the question for each trophic level, and found broad patterns of population control. They reasoned that decomposers as a group are limited by food since by definition their function is to assimilate organic debris. As for producers, only in rare cases are green plants depleted by herbivores. What most frequently limits plant species, as a group, whether in the deprived Arctic or in the struggles of plant succession, is light. Where it is not light, as in arid lands, the limiting factor is water. In a few cases, where both light and moisture are sufficient, then lack of a mineral becomes the limiting factor. Like decomposers, producers also are resource-limited.

Herbivores, to the contrary, apparently are rarely in want of forage. The exhaustion of the Kaibab deer range was brought about by unnatural conditions. And while occasional plagues of locusts or rodents consume their resources, the general rule is: herbivore populations are controlled by predators. It follows that the limiting factor for carnivores is availability of meat, their food. (Hence the importance of being an omnivore like humans and rats.)

Since decomposers, producers, and predators generally are resource-limited, the various species must either compete directly for the common resource or make some accommodation to share it. Decomposers, about which least is known, use antibiosis to fight off competitors. Antibiosis is a mechanism by which an organism produces a compound that inhibits the growth of other organisms or destroys them. More is known about antibiosis in plants; it is believed to play a part in keeping vegetation widely separated in the desert where each plant needs a relatively large area to collect moisture in order to survive. Algae, fungi, molds, and bacteria are all known to produce antibiotics. And, of course, the penicillin secreted by the bread mold *Penicillium notatum* is one of the staples of modern medicine.

Plants also compete for space (the *sine qua non* for light, water, and minerals) through crowding and shading. Or, space can be captured and occupied through specialization. As various species have become best adapted to particular requirements, we see vegetational zonation geographically or horizontally in forest stratification or temporally in seasonal succession.

4

In the early 1920s, Russian biologist G. F. Gause studied competition in ecology's first milestone laboratory experiments. Gause undertook to see what would happen when two closely related protozoan species, *Paramecium caudatum* and *Paramecium aurelia*, shared the same environment and competed for the same resource—a food culture of bacteria. When placed in the culture medium separately, each species developed according to the typical sigmoidal growth curve, leveling off with a constant population. When placed together, the paramecia followed the same growth pattern for the first six to eight days; then the *P. caudatum* began to diminish, *P. aurelia* to increase. At the end of 16 days, only *P. aurelia* survived.

In this competition, neither organism attacked the other or secreted harmful substances. But *P. aurelia* proved less sensitive to the bacteria's waste products and had a higher intrinsic growth rate. Thus it took ever more of the limited food as its more successful population expanded.

In a long series of experiments, Thomas Park of the University of Chicago measured competition in relation to environment by examining two species of flour beetles under varied conditions. In every case, one or the other species always was eliminated. In a hot and wet climate, the beetle *Tribolium castaneum* survived 100 percent of the time. Under cool-dry conditions, *Tribolium confusum* survived 100 percent of the time. In a hot-dry mixture, *T. confusum* survived in 90 percent of the experiments, but when the environmental conditions were switched to cool-wet, *T. confusum*'s success dropped to about 70 percent.

Gause himself found that when he pitted *P. caudatum* against *P. aurelia* in a non-bacterial culture medium, *P. caudatum* became the surviving population. This phenomenon, that species with the same niche requirements cannot coexist, came to be known as the principle of competitive exclusion or Gause's law.

Surprisingly, this all-or-nothing outcome of interspecific

competition does not lead to a reduction of species, but quite the reverse. Gause wrote:

"There is in nature a great diversity of 'niches' with different conditions, and in one niche the first competitor possessing advantages over the second will displace him, but in another niche with different conditions the advantages will belong to the second species which will completely displace the first. Therefore side by side in one community, but occupying somewhat different niches, two or more nearly related species will continue to live in a certain state of equilibrium."

If that first sentence seems familiar, like a restatement of Darwin's theory that any slight variation which better adapts an individual to his environment will give him a better chance for survival, then Darwin himself had a chance to observe the validity of the second sentence nearly a century earlier on the Galapagos Islands.

Those islands, 600 miles west of the South American mainland and supporting a range of environment from desert to moist forest, were a natural evolutionary laboratory. On these isolated islands, Darwin found 14 species of finches, many of them unlike any he had seen before. One species could pluck a long spine from a cactus and hold it in its beak to probe the cactus for insects.

How did all these species come about? This is how George Woodwell explains the process in terms of modern ecology: Surmising that some finches survived from flocks of birds wind-carried westward from South America to the islands which were free of predators and rich in a variety of food, Dr. Woodwell goes on:

"Reproducing rapidly, each new immigrant population became a plague, much as the Japanese beetle, the sparrow, the starling, the gypsy moth, and a host of other introductions have become plagues in our own experience. Food, although at first abundant, quickly became limiting, and the struggle for existence intensified. Competition for food was fierce and a premium attached to any ability to exploit new food supplies—foods different from those exploited by competitors. Small differences in behavior or in size or shape of beak resulted in small differences in survival and in ability to rear young. These differences, when hereditary and useful, were passed on and amplified in the population, and on each island there developed a population of finches peculiarly adapted to that environment and different from populations on the other islands.

"There was one additional complication. Exchanges of individuals or small groups of individuals occurred occasionally among the islands, continually testing the degree of genetic isolation achieved by the evolution of different races. Frequently these transported populations failed on the new island or were absorbed into the now-indigenous population; occasionally, however, a small one found itself partially isolated ecologically, by behavior, food supply, or local preference of habitat, from the indigenous population and survived as a distinct population, competition and evolution tending to accentuate the isolating mechanisms. Thus the islands gradually acquired a diverse bird fauna consisting largely of races of finches: ground finches, tree finches, a warbler finch, a woodpecker finch—each race using a set of resources used elsewhere in the world by a totally different species. Ecologists call the resources used by any one species a niche; where niches overlap and resources are shared, they say that competition occurs.

"We see from this example, which is a grossly simplified version of *Darwin's Finches*, that the evolution of life proceeds toward reduction of competition, toward utilization of space and other resources, toward diversity in form and function, toward filling of niches."

In Hawaii, 14 species of honeycreepers have evolved, from nectar feeders to woodpeckers. The black-capped chickadee is common in eastern North America where it has no competition from closely related birds. But in Europe, where there are several other similar species, the black-cap is restricted to swamp forests during breeding season; the other species live in the kinds of forests that chickadees occupy in the States.

And so it appears that species are a response to niches, a species being the kind of plant or animal that can use one or more resources in a particular way more effectively than any competitors. An ecological niche, says Professor Odum, is an organism's profession. In order to understand any organism's position in the community, we must know how it makes a living (or gets its energy), whom it has contacts with, what effect it has upon the ecosystem, as well as a fact sheet on its metabolism, growth rate, and so forth.

Professor G. Evelyn Hutchinson of Yale University sees the niche as a set of unique multidimensional physical-chemical-biological conditions within which a particular species can live. Regarded in this way the role of niche and the principle of competitive exclusion appear as a complex homologue of the physical law that two objects cannot occupy the same space at the same time.

Evidence that niches invite species is provided by what are called ecological equivalents. Darwin's finches are one example. A finch in the Galapagos performs the role of the woodpecker in the United States. The cactus of the American southwestern desert and the euphorbia of African deserts are both succulent, spiny, flowering plants adapted to arid conditions. Their appearance is so similar that the amateur cannot distinguish between them. Yet each belongs to a different family of plants.

There are no jack rabbits on the grassland pampas of

Argentina. But there is the cavy, an animal that looks like a jack rabbit and acts like a jack rabbit, but taxonomically is related to the guinea pig. The carnivorous snake niche is occupied by the mussarama in South America, the hamadryad in India, and the king snake in the United States. In Australia, marsupials fill the niches taken in other parts of the world by placental mammals, undoubtedly because Australia became isolated from the mainland before placental mammals developed in Asia. In Australia, marsupials—any pouched animal, like the opossum—resemble cats, mice, moles, sloths, squirrels, and groundhogs. The Tasmanian wolf looks like a wolf, runs down prey like a wolf, kills like a wolf, but sometimes jumps like the kangaroo to which it is related.

In the mature climax forest ecosystem, most if not all of the niches have been filled. There is no longer surplus or excess energy—it is being consumed through the existing plexus of circuits, sustaining maximum kinds and numbers of organisms. Alterations occur only with environmental changes favoring new or presently subordinate species and with the invasion of some species that aggressively takes over a niche. But generally, this is more difficult to accomplish in a tightly knit society.

Paleoecologist Paul Martin has pointed to open niches in the United States that could be filled for more efficient use of energy in a hungry world. One million square miles of browse land in southwestern and western United States and in Mexico—the semi-arid brush eschewed by grazing cattle and sheep—could support 15 to 30 million animals, Dr. Martin estimates. A prime candidate, he suggests, is the African eland which is becoming an important domestic food animal in South Africa.

The U.S. Army used camels in the Southwest in the 1850s. The camels immediately recognized an open niche when they saw one. The reason that the camels were so at home in the terrain could be that their prehistoric ancestors originated there. An army officer, George Beale, wrote of the camels: "As soon as they arrive they are turned loose to graze, but appear to prefer to browse on the mesquite bushes and the leaves of a thorny shrub, which grows in this country everywhere, to the finest grass."

Evolution then, can be seen as a biological response to niche requirements. If conditions change, then the species must adapt to the new requirements through selection and hereditary adaptation. The British hedgehog, a spiny mammal somewhat like the American porcupine, traditionally has reacted to danger by coming to a dead stop and rolling into a spiny ball. Obviously, it is an ill-conceived tactic against an oncoming automobile and particularly, since the hedgehog is a nocturnal animal, at night. Recently, naturalists in Lancashire have reported seeing a hedgehog *run* from autos. In another decade, they predicted, *all* Lancashire hedgehogs will be using this more successful method to defend against autos.

5

If conditions change too radically or, more precisely, too radically too quickly, then a species may not be able to meet the challenge through the gradual mechanism of evolution. The ginkgo is a tree species that has existed on earth for 200 million years, probably because it is extremely resistant to insects. But the ginkgo is only fairly resistant to air pollution and is threatened by our present environment. In 1800, there were an estimated five *billion* passenger pigeons in the United States. One ornithologist observed a flock 240 miles long. That was in 1810. In September,

1914, Martha, the last carrier pigeon, died in a Cincinnati zoo. The species became extinct because of overhunting, destruction of the northern beech forests, and the phenomenon that some populations below a certain critical number cannot survive.

This principle—that populations with too few individuals may not survive—is manifested in many ways. The reduction in numbers cuts down the chance of members of the species meeting and mating. This principle underlies the campaign against malaria. The goal is to allow the emergence of a human population appreciably free of the parasite. As the percentage of malaria carriers dwindles, it becomes increasingly difficult for the parasites to move to new host via the random mosquito conveyance.

The principle is probably best illustrated in reverse by the necessity of many plant and animal species to gather into groups. The clustering of bees enables the massed individuals to generate enough heat to survive the low temperatures that would kill isolated individuals. During a winter's night, bobwhite quail mass in a tight circle with some perched on others in a tableau of survival. It has been found that if the covey is reduced beyond a critical level by hunting, all the quail perish. Fish have a much better chance to escape a predator in a school than alone—even the frequency of encounters is diminished. When a group of pronghorn antelope numbers 16 or more members, the herd will stand its ground against a wolf attack.

This formation of groups—or clumping, as it is called in ecology—is part of another characteristic of a population: its form of distribution, or dispersion. Clumping is apparent among plants with seeds of low mobility whereas goldenrod with highly mobile seeds may take root in a random distribution. Clumping is common among mammals since even families come under this heading. In addition to clumping and random, there may be a uniform dispersion, which can be accomplished through territoriality.

Even when mammals or birds gather into herds or flocks, however, close observation will disclose that individuals of many species maintain a spacing within the group, which is known as individual distance. The many elaborate courtship rituals—from the vainglory of peacocks to the cautious lulling of the black widow spider—are designed to overcome the individual distance barrier.

In interspecific meetings, wild animals observe a flight distance and an attack distance. While camouflage, protective armor, or offensive odor are some methods of dealing with predators, flight is the basic mechanism for mobile organisms. Generally, the larger the animal, the greater its flight distance—an antelope will flee from an intruder 500 yards away, a wall lizard's flight distance is six feet. But when the intruder approaches to within a critical distance, the flight pattern turns to attack. For a rhinoceros, which is short-sighted and aggressive, the attack distance is considerable. A lion in a zoo will flee from an approaching man until it reaches a barrier. If the man continues to close the distance, the lion reverses direction and begins to stalk the

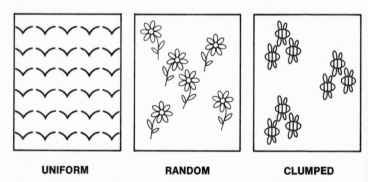

UNIFORM   **RANDOM**   **CLUMPED**

THREE BASIC SPACING PATTERNS OF INDIVIDUALS IN A POPULATION

man. "In the classical animal act in the circus," Edward Hall writes in his book about spacing, *The Hidden Dimension*, "the lion's stalking is so deliberate that he will surmount an intervening obstacle such as a stool in order to get at the man. To get the lion to remain on the stool, the lion tamer quickly steps out of the critical zone. At this point, the lion stops pursuing. The trainer's elaborate 'protective' devices—the chair, the whip, or the gun—are so much window dressing."

All organisms need a certain amount of space, critical space, in order to survive. Overcrowding or the breaching of this space requirement can itself be a limiting factor in population. This is the final population characteristic—density, which is the measure of individuals of a species in a certain area. When the rabbit population reaches a certain density, there is a large die-off from "shock disease," which corresponds to the stress syndrome Hans Selye has reported in humans. It is a functional breakdown of the adrenalin-pituitary system brought about by overcrowding and most evident in cyclic mammals.

There is a perfectly reasonable explanation for what happens. The hare survives by constant vigilance. After the population reaches a certain density, there are so many in any particular area that each individual is continually being startled. In response to this constant psychological stress, the adrenal gland overproduces, to the animal's destruction.

In studies of voles, whose population also swings sharply in cycles, it was found that a die-off from intolerable density was accompanied by strife during the breeding season, causing the death of young and a psychological derangement among adults. Another die-off was characterized by exhaustion of the adrenal and pituitary functions, liver degeneration, and cannibalism. Cannibalism as a method of population control is common to a wide range of fish, rodents, and birds.

In contrast to the Kaibab deer population which crashed because of lack of food, Sika deer on James Island in Chesapeake Bay were well fed, free of parasites, and still suffered a 60 percent die-off. Four or five deer were placed on the 280-acre island in 1916. By 1955, the population had reached 280 to 300 deer. In 1958, the population crashed. Examination of the dead deer, particularly the young, showed signs of adrenal exhaustion and hepatitis and nephritis, two diseases closely related to adrenal malfunctioning.

High density also is known to reduce natality as well as increase mortality. Richard Van Gelder of the American Museum of Natural History cites the case of two confined groups of African elephants. One group is crammed into a sanctuary near Murchison Falls at a density that might be considered cruelty to animals—ten to the square mile. The elephants are destroying their habitat, says Dr. Van Gelder, but they remain because they have learned what happens to them if they go outside. At another preserve, elephants have a density of two per square mile, still too high for elephants but an improvement over the first refuge.

In the relatively low density area, the young are weaned at eight years of age. The female gives birth to her first offspring at 12, then reproduces once every seven years. Since an elephant lives from 50 to 70 years, each female averages six offspring.

In the high density area near Murchison Falls, the young are not weaned until they are 10 years old. The female does not reproduce until she is 20 and then breeds every 12 years. This combination of delayed beginning of reproduction and longer spacing reduces the number of offspring per female to three and cuts the population growth rate by two-thirds.

Australian ecologist A. J. Nicholson says, "Populations are self-governing systems. They regulate their densities in relation to their own properties and those of their environments."

These internal checks on population, irrespective of food limitations, are mechanisms of which Thomas Malthus was unaware. The wood stork, for example, breeds when the water levels are falling and the small fish on which it feeds become concentrated and easy to catch in the shallow pools. If the water level remains high during the dry season or fails to rise in the wet season to ensure a good supply of fish, the stork will not nest.

In Switzerland, the alpine swift population maintains a constant reproduction rate of two and three-quarters chicks per nest. This constancy is achieved in the following manner. The population is made up of twice as many three-egg layers as two-egg layers. However, broods of three are about twice as likely to starve to death in the nest. In four-egg nests, the advantage gained by the extra egg is offset by the extra work needed to feed four nestlings—the chances are two in five in these cases that the whole brood will be lost.

Territoriality is a well-studied method of population control practiced by many birds and mammals. Territorial individuals subdivide an area into smaller plots that are defended instinctively or compulsively, not as a matter of conscious decision. Commonly, the boundary of a territory is marked with sewage disposal—urine and feces. The tiger uses what Dr. Van Gelder calls the railroad track system. The big cat leaves an odor on the trail as he passes. If the scent still is strong, a second tiger coming along will know that someone has just preceded him, and take another route. The strength of the redolence corresponds to a red, yellow, or green light for the next tiger. In the case of howler monkeys, the territory is delineated with sound— the monkeys' calls and shrieks, rather than odors, marking the boundaries.

In an experiment with house mice in England, it was found that when they all were enclosed in a single cage, pregnancies simply ceased after the population reached a certain density. But when mice were moved to large rings set up in an aircraft hangar, the pattern of territoriality appeared as soon as there were two males. Ultimately, there were five territories defended by five males with their harems. All the remaining mice were crowded into a communal area. At first, the population skyrocketed. Then natality was affected in the communal area, in a definite order: first, higher mortality among the young. Second, a decrease in the number of young born. Finally, an end to ovulation. Thereafter, reproduction took place only in the territories, and the population stabilized.

Observations in a savannah woodland in Australia of black-backed magpies showed a similar pattern. The territorial birds occupied the choice woodland, with loose flocks confined to treeless grassland. Breeding took place only among the territorial birds. Young birds and sometimes breeding females returned to the flock. From time to time, members of the flock tried to take over territories, usually unsuccessfully. During breeding season the ovaries of former territorial birds were found to be less well developed than those of females in the territories. In effect, the functioning population maintained a floating reserve from which it drew replacements when needed.

Not only does territoriality provide population control, but the uniform dispersion guarantees a maximum use of resources. In a series of experiments with blowflies, Dr. Nicholson found that when individuals of a species were forced to "scramble" for their food under heavily crowded conditions, the resource was in effect wasted. Each competitor got so little of the food that it was unable to survive and make a contribution to the population. Scrambling tended to cause violent oscillations in the population.

Territoriality also reduces violence between individuals through well-understood rules and ritualized encounters.

Animals accomplish a similar reduction of competition and violence through dominance hierarchy, most commonly known as a peck order because the behavior was first noticed in chickens. Other social hierarchies vary from this straight linear ranking, but like territoriality the design permits maximum use of resources and controls crowding through institutionalized bluff and threat with a minimum of energy wasted in fighting. Naturalist Bil Gilbert has written that fighting takes place among dogs only when there is a misunderstanding or honest difference of opinion as to which animal is the social superior. Konrad Lorenz, the famous exponent of the science of animal behavior or ethology, also discloses that no canine can deliberately kill a member of its species that offers its jugular in submission.

Social dominance and hierarchy seem to be one counterbalance to the force that brings many species together in groups. When this crowding—necessary for protection, reproduction, or environmental reasons—becomes too dense, aggressiveness increases. Young groundhogs spend their youth avoiding aggressive adults and as a result move away to new habitats. John Christian, who has spent many years studying animal populations and behavior patterns, sees social dominance behavior as an important instrument in evolution. The combination of population density and intraspecific competition, he says, has been a powerful force in species dispersal. Since the socially dominant individuals control the habitat, it is the socially subordinate members that are forced to emigrate—usually to less favorable environments at their risk. But those who survive under the new conditions provide material for new races through selection and genetic variation.

"Such a behavioral mechanism," Dr. Christian says, "seems appropriate to explain the evolutionary events that have resulted in the present 14 species of finches in the Galapagos Island."

So dispersal is still another way to regulate populations. The technique of emigration is employed in spectacular fashion by lemmings. "The lemmings march chiefly at night," wrote Charles Elton, "and may traverse more than a hundred miles of country before reaching the sea, into which they plunge unhesitatingly, and continue to swim on until they die. Even then they float, so that their dead bodies form drifts on the seashore. This migration, a very remarkable performance for an animal the size of a small rat ... is caused primarily by over-population in their mountain home, and the migrations are a symptom of maximum in numbers which is always terminated by a severe epidemic; and this reduces the population to a very few individuals."

Man has played an important part in the opposite form of plant and animal dispersal, immigration into an area. The effects are seen most dramatically on islands where ecosystems are simpler and less resistant to invaders. Approximately one half of the 180 major pests in the United States come from beyond its borders. The exotic walking catfish was imported into Florida by tropical fish dealers, then several specimens literally walked away to freedom and now contend with native fish in many of south Florida's waterways. The chestnut blight, caused by a parasitic fungus, was brought into New York City from Asia on nursery plants in 1908. Most of the chestnut trees in the eastern forest were dead by 1950.

The sea lamprey operated on a slower timetable. This predator, which normally lives in the ocean but spawns in streams, had navigated the St. Lawrence River and established itself in Lake Ontario, but had been blocked from advancing farther by the cataract at Niagara Falls. The Welland Canal was opened in 1829 bypassing the Falls into Lake Erie. Probably because the streams were not right for spawning and for other reasons, the sea lamprey did not multiply in Lake Erie.

But in 1930 lampreys were seen in the St. Clair River and seven years later in Lake Michigan. The sea lamprey clamps its mouth onto its prey, then secretes an anticoagulant and other fluids into the open wound, rasping and sucking the victim's flesh and juices. The prey may last a week or sometimes succumbs in hours. Sea lampreys apparently will take on any size prey: one attached itself to a porthole window of the research submarine *Ben Franklin* during a dive off the Atlantic shelf.

In Lake Michigan, the lampreys virtually wiped out the lake trout. Not only was a choice fishery destroyed, but the loss of the trout weakened the ecological stability of the lake, compounding the process of eutrophication caused by massive dumping of wastes and pollution caused by drainage of persistent pesticides. With their predators, the trout, gone, alewives at once took advantage of the situation by multiplying egregiously. The alewives were able to do this because, in addition to the absence of predators, the eutrophic lake offered a generous food supply. However, the alewife population grew to be so huge that there were massive die-offs for various reasons, some of them not fully understood. Suddenly there were masses of dead, stinking fish along the Lake Michigan shoreline. At this point, the problem no longer was simply ecological; it was also political.

"*Do* something," aroused members of the now involved human species told their leaders, a command that was much more easily issued than carried out. As it happened, an inspired ecological solution resolved the problem. Coho salmon were imported from the West Coast and implanted into the lake. The salmon knew an open ecological niche when they found one, and filled it; specifically they began gobbling up alewives as desired. The salmon did so well, in fact, that something unforeseen happened—a multi-million dollar sport fishing industry suddenly bloomed around Lake Michigan. Unfortunately, there was still one more unanticipated development . . . but that's another story and will be told later.

Salmon, like sea lampreys, normally spawn in fresh water streams and live in the ocean. They are known as anadromous fish. A dam built across a river that blocks the passage of the salmon to their particular spawning area means annihilation for that population, for the salmon will reproduce only in the stream in which they were born. In order to get around this impediment, engineers have built steps on dams to help the salmon using the Columbia River. However, there now are or will be so many dams on the river that despite the fantastic motivation and stamina that enable salmon to reach their necessary headwaters, the prospects of the future survival of the Columbia River population seemed poor. To avert that possibility, fisheries biologists have set up hatcheries near the river, captured some migrant salmon and began spawning in the hatcheries. The fascinating result of this experiment is that salmon spawned in hatcheries now return to the hatcheries to reproduce.

Back and forth migration is the third form of population

dispersal. Although commonly observed in birds and fish, this activity is poorly understood; undoubtedly it enables many species to exploit unused resources and permits a population size that would otherwise be insupportable.

6

Recently, two aerodynamic specialists calculated that large migrating birds flying in V-formation have 71 percent more range than a bird flying alone. The updraft from the wing tips gives a boost to the next bird. Now there is speculation that much of the honking during migratory flights comes from birds working extra hard; they are ordering squadron mates back into proper formation.

And this introduces the final major strategy for survival —cooperation. This has been alluded to in a number of ways. The members of a species that herd together are cooperating. So are the fungi and algae that live together in the symbiotic arrangement of the lichen. The mutualism is essential to the survival of both species. There are many such examples of mutualism. The nitrogen-fixing bacteria have found a home in the roots of legumes, and have proved to be very beneficial tenants. The damsel fish or sea clown lures prey to within the poisonous clutches of the sea anemone; for its part, the stationary animal hides the fishes' eggs and removes parasites with its tentacles. The yucca moth is the sole means of pollinating yucca plants. Termites could not survive without certain wood-digesting protozoa bivouacked in their intestines.

Even where parasites are feeding off a host, a gradual *modus vivendi* is achieved reducing the harmful consequences of this competitive symbiotic relationship. The sickle-shaped blood cells that produce a severe anemia in

Negroes are the result of a defensive adaptation to the malarial parasite developed during the course of evolutionary time. The abnormal hemoglobin and cells can carry less oxygen, but they do confer a high degree of resistance to malaria—so the inherited trait is beneficial in Africa but a handicap in the United States where it cuts in half the lifespan of one in every 500 Negroes.

With pathogens, the stories are legion—when first introduced, they tear through a population with high virulence, but later subside into low-grade infections. In 1950, the Australian government introduced the disease myxomatosis into the rabbit population. The first outbreak of the disease killed up to 99 percent of Australia's rabbits. The second resulted in a mortality of 85 to 95 percent; the third killed from 40 to 60 percent of the rabbit population. The rabbit and the myxomatosis virus populations headed toward ecological stability. The rabbits developed a genetic resistance to the disease through survival of the most resistant individuals whose traits were passed to offspring and then spread through the population.

At the same time, a milder strain of virus began outcompeting the more virulent form. This came about because the virus survives by being transmitted to its next host by a mosquito. Naturally, the more virulent strain kills its host rabbit more quickly; but this reduces the time and opportunity for a mosquito vector to carry the disease to the next rabbit. Conversely, the attenuated virus permits its host to live or live longer and enhances its own chances for spreading and surviving.

The Hawaiian Islands supported a native population of 300,000 men and women in splendid isolation until the arrival of Captain Cook in 1778. Thereafter disease eroded the numbers. Epidemics of measles, pertuisis, and influenza killed every child born in 1848. By 1860, the population of

native Hawaiians had fallen to less than 37,000. The King
and Queen of Hawaii were stricken and died of measles
during a royal visit to London in 1824, René Dubos observes in *Mirage of Health*. "Sir Henry Halford, president of
the Royal College of Physicians, and the two other attending English doctors found it difficult to believe that a disease 'which even a delicate London girl might bear could be
so destructive to robust denizens of the Pacific.' "

Beyond adaptation or accommodation, beyond *modus
vivendi*, there is a cooperation built into natural systems.
Naturalist Bil Gilbert, while on a hawk-banding assignment
in the mountains of western Pennsylvania, described one
species' danger signals that can't help but aid other creatures as well:

"The chickadees give a sharp, insistent danger call. This
call is easily distinguishable from the one these birds give in
response to danger which they discover on the ground, and
much different from the alarm they give when they see a
hawk trapper approaching the blind. The call of the first
chickadee is taken up by the rest of the flock. The closer the
hawk approaches, the sharper and more insistent are the
calls of our sentinels.

"When the hawk is close to the blind, even though we
may not be able to see him, we are able to make a good
guess at what species he is by 'reading' the signs of the
chickadees.

"Red-tailed hawks are the species which most frequently
come to our nets. They are large birds (sometimes their
wingspread is nearly five feet), but relatively slow and
clumsy. A red-tail has practically no chance of capturing a
small, agile bird. The chickadees seem to realize this. They
continue their warning call as the hawk approaches, and
keep it up while he is over the pines, even when he is in the
net. Occasionally, however, we are visited by an accipiter

hawk. This group is represented by three species in the United States—sharp-shins, Cooper's hawks, and goshawks. All three are slim-bodied, quick, and very maneuverable. Their natural prey is birds, which they are well equipped to pursue and capture. When one of the accipiters approaches, the chickadees begin to call, but the alarm note is different. We can recognize more panic in the note. The certain sign to us that an accipiter is approaching is not a sound but the sudden lack of it. When the accipiter sweeps directly over the pine grove, the chickadees and other birds become abruptly silent and do not move or become vocal until the hawk has disappeared."

A three-year ecological study of the Wilpattu National Park in Ceylon documented the habits of the leopard. The top predator in the park kills 3,400 pounds of meat a year and consumes about one ton of it. Scavengers get the rest. The leopard kills 50 percent of the newborn swine during their first five weeks of life and 80 percent of the young axis deer during their first year. Occasionally, the leopard takes monkeys, other deer, and hare to supplement its fare.

"People don't like the leopard because he kills," says the leader of the 13-man study, John Eisenberg of Washington's National Zoological Park-Smithsonian Institution. "But they don't understand that there is a natural overpopulation of animals to account for illness and predation. The goal of nature is zero population growth, and only man violates that goal. The prey needs the predator as much as the predator needs the prey. Without the leopard, the other animals would be miserable. They would be crowded and would not be able to feed themselves."

The American mountain lion also feeds on deer. "Old deer, very young deer, sick deer, wounded deer," writes naturalist-author Edward Abbey, "the culls and leavings of the herd. In this process of natural selection, given a liberal allowance of time, it is the lion's claw, the lion's tooth and need, which has given the deer its beauty, speed and grace."

There are three paradoxes in natural systems, in which, as in some expert sleight of hand, cooperation emerges magically from competition. On the intraspecific level—where members of the same population compete—the individual is dispensable so that the species may survive, the individual is sacrificed in order that the species may prosper.

As a corollary, the individual is important only as a functioning member of a population and community. The leopard lives to be about 12 or 15 years old in captivity, but survives no more than 10 years in the wild, Dr. Eisenberg says, because of disease and injuries suffered in fighting. "The predator has to be in top-flight condition. An injury impairs his ability to kill, which means he can't eat." In nature, there are no free rides. No retirement with a pension after 20 years. No retirement, period.

The second paradox—on the interspecific level—is that while each species single-mindedly pursues its own ends, it contributes to the welfare of other populations. Without the leopard, the axis deer repeat the lesson of the Kaibab Plateau. The green plant fixes energy for its own use and feeds the world.

The third paradox is that a system of obligatory cooperation appears out of a basic conflict for existence. Instead of interminable warfare, natural systems have found ways to avoid or reduce competition and in so doing to enlarge the use of resources. With elaboration of niches and species, interdependence grows out of confrontation. There are many strands in the web, many alternatives, many feedbacks—many chances to change, to adjust, to compensate. The ecosystem's survival, finally, depends upon no one species, but the loss of any species weakens the totality.

That seems to be the grand strategy for survival in natural biological systems. Simplicity risks vulnerability, complexity enhances stability. A closed system by necessity seeking to be a durable system through providence becomes a diverse system.

CHAPTER FIVE

Epilogue and Prologue

1

THESE WERE the salient findings of ecology in the 20th century. While they were interesting discoveries that nature certainly is a wonderful mechanism, to popular opinion they were so *peripheral*. After all, while these quaint ecologists were hip-deep in some godforsaken marsh somewhere, chemists were making it big in pharmaceuticals and creating a billion-dollar niche for their employers in the agriculture industry (interspecific defense against bacterial, parasitic, and insect enemies). The high-energy physicists went sailing down the main channel with their cyclotrons in tow (intraspecific defense against human enemies). There was no lack of funds for these barons of Berkeley whenever they wanted to manufacture another element with a lifetime of a microsecond. Treasure poured into medical research helped make physicians the wealthiest class in the United States (defense against disease).

The reasons for the largesse were obvious to the rulers of the scientific establishment and the pragmatic disbursers in Washington. These pursuits could enhance America's health, wealth, or power. What could lemming-counters or weed-watchers contribute?

As a matter of fact, their fellow biologists—following

F. H. Crick, J. D. Watson, and DNA—were trooping and snooping in the opposite direction, seeking life's secrets in ever smaller dimensions. The way to find ultimate reality was through a microscope, preferably an electron microscope. The atomism of Democritus, triumphant in physics, now was storming biology.

Moreover, this approach had the irresistible momentum of success. Most of the astounding accomplishments of modern science and technology stemmed from one technique: the analytical method. Taking things apart to find out what makes them tick. Breaking units down to study their component parts. Compartmentalizing, pigeon-holing, concentrating on parts. Analysis is a household word, from urine to psycho. It is not an exaggeration to say that our Western civilization is built upon this principle.

Analysis is a tough method to beat in attacking a problem. It concentrates maximum effort upon each small area. It allows magnificatoin of focus. It remains manageable. It permits redundancy to eliminate oversights or slip-ups.

But the method has a weakness. While it establishes experts, it imprisons them.

The chemist who makes DDT or the entomologist who advises how to use it would not consider himself an authority on what the pesticide does to the porpoise population. Indeed, it would never occur to either of them to think about such a matter. Again, while the Agriculture Department takes to heart the welfare of agriculture, it may ignore the welfare of all other Americans. That's as it should be under analytic discipline. HEW is supposed to look after the others.

As a result of this approach, the Federal Government in 1970 discovered it had 84 different agencies that dealt with environment, many of them, naturally, working at cross purposes. While the Agriculture Department in 1969 paid

farmers three and a half billion dollars to refrain from production, the Interior Department's Bureau of Reclamation
spent 85 million dollars for irrigation projects to bring arid
lands of the West into production.

Theodore H. White wrote of the Federal jungle: "Almost
each of the 80-odd agencies which shared management of
the American environment had a history of its own, crusted
over with an entrenched lobby, an entrenched congressional
committee, an entrenched bureaucracy, each ferociously de-
fending its own prerogatives. Such bureaus had been born
variously of a national crisis, a public outrage, a scientist's
insight or a President's dream—but all reflected that hoary
first principle of American government: when something
itches, scratch it."

Creating specialists was probably the only way to deal
with an ever-ramifying body of knowledge and information.
It was no more than imitating the solution of nature, the
architect of specialists (although man is the unexcelled generalist). But by the mass resort to the analytic method,
civilization created a race of experts who by training, by
tradition, by habit, and by inclination *do not think in terms
of wholes.*

The men who traditionally think in broad, general terms
—philosophers, theologians, poets—have been so outcom-
peted in status and influence by the analytic method and its
specialists that when a television broadcast occasionally
needs a "wise" man, it taps a psychiatrist.

The analytic method also is unsuited to thinking in terms
of process. Analysis is stop-action, frozen events, discrete
packages. The essence of living systems is process—cycles,
circulation, interactions, reaction, succession, evolution.

Commonly, the opposite of analysis is thought of as synthesis—putting things together. But men, so far at least,
have not been adept at the synthetic method. Philosophi-

cally, it has not been productive. Industrially, we are very good at producing a billion bottles or 100 million autos, but inept when it comes to synthesizing them back into something.

As it happens, there is another opposite to the analytic method, known as holism: seeing things as wholes, the belief that a whole unit is something more than the sum of its parts, that there is a functional or organic relationship between the parts and the whole that is lost in dissection.

Marston Bates gave an example of this principle in *The Forest and the Sea.* "Cultures of tissues in the laboratory can be kept alive indefinitely if care is taken to provide nourishment, to remove waste products, and to cut away excessive growth to prevent overcrowding. But so far we have not been able to keep the organism itself alive indefinitely—death, then, is a property not of the life-stuff, but of the organization."

From their studies of natural systems, ecologists came to adopt the holistic view as the only way to comprehend their subject. A forest was something more than a collection of squirrels and pine trees. The forest ecosystem exerted a profound effect upon all component life in the area and could affect the environment a thousand miles away. Furthermore, ecologists found that the analytic method simply cannot cope with effects produced by alterations in a complex organization. Build a canal to help commerce between Lake Ontario and Lake Erie and a century later you lose a trout fishery in Lake Michigan. Have a bad volcanic eruption, six years later you get a world-wide flu epidemic. Help the deer by killing their predators, you ruin the deer's habitat. Common-sense reasoning or conventional logic didn't help much in these situations either.

From their studies ecologists also absorbed into their psyches the importance of environment to living systems and things. The organism and population *always* exist in symbiosis with environment: their welfare and survival depend upon it absolutely. It is one of those ironies of history that at the moment their fellow men were experiencing the euphoria of omnipotence from manipulating and exploiting their environment, ecologists were detecting the signs of impending calamity.

At first, when ecologists began pointing to dangers, their warnings were ignored. A scientific paper usually addresses itself to a modest area; it is usually read only by fellow scientists. This is the way scientific knowledge is advanced, in little steps on a broad front with ample time for questioning, corroborating, and cross checking. Rachel Carson's *Silent Spring* was not a brief paper, it was a book; not a single shot directed against one isolated target, but a broadside against the use of pesticides and involving a very remunerative industry; not a scientific paper for the eyes of only the initiated, but a national bestseller. Miss Carson's attack could not be ignored. Nothing was done about her charges because no one could show that pesticides, used properly, were directly harmful to man.

A second attack, against the analytic method as exemplified by molecular biology and the general indifference of science to the deterioration of the environment, came with Barry Commoner's book, *Science and Survival.*

As it turned out, the ecological indictment was vindicated in surprisingly short order. Public opinion was shocked into accepting the validity of ecologists' contentions by the string of concussions from *Torrey Canyon's* sinking, Lake Erie, Santa Barbara, seizure of DDT-contaminated salmon in Lake Michigan, the Everglades, smog in the eyes, jet noise in the ears, traffic jam in the nerves. For some strange reason, the system was running amuck.

But it is doubtful that anyone appreciates what the price

may be in seeking solutions from ecology. Americans have indicated a willingness to set aside a reasonable amount of tax revenues to clean up the environment. They might even accept some inconveniences. But what if the price is the overthrow of the presumptions, premises, the very foundations of Western beliefs? Or subordinating the authority of all man-oriented sciences?

We have already seen that the once-absolute authority of the marketplace has been eroded by the acids in polluted waterways. What if the challenge is to the primacy of the state itself? What if the price is the sovereignty of man?

PART TWO

Beating the System

CHAPTER SIX

Ecce Homo: *Behold the Man*

1

LIFE BEGAN ON EARTH about three billion years ago, one and a half billion years after the earth itself. A chemical evolution had been taking place for a long time before the biological one. Astronomers now are finding what are believed to be such early life ingredients as formaldehyde and hydrogen cyanide in the clouds of space. For millions of years preceding the beginning of life, ever larger and more complex molecules—amino acids, perhaps primitive proteins, and other carbon compounds—had been forming in the primeval seas. Strong unscreened solar radiation and lightning flashes in the primal atmosphere perhaps made up of methane, ammonia, hydrogen, and water could have supplied the ingredients and combinations for the transition to an organism that could reproduce itself. With the formation of nucleic acid, this became possible.

It is likely that there were a number of experiments that failed. But finally a one-celled organism, something like our present-day bacteria, got started in the thin soup of organic material that clouded the ancient seas. The primordial creature was a heterotroph, what we now classify as a decomposer. It lived upon the organic matter that would

141

correspond roughly to "dead" material except that it had never lived.

This method of existence—consuming non-renewable resources—was an exploitive economy that was not to be repeated until the civilization of man. The scarcity of the practice is understandable since it is incompatible with longevity.

So with this progenitor, life appeared destined for a limited regime. But evolution and speciation began their work and during this process autotrophs with the ability to photosynthesize food energy were born. With their arrival began the simplest kind of an ecosystem, the potentiality for a balanced, non-exploitive economy and an open-ended future.

Life had ascended so far along the evolutionary ladder that with the beginning of the Cambrian period, the earliest division of the Paleozoic era, about 600 million years ago, animals began developing hard shells and other parts which left a much better fossil record. The Paleozoic was born with upheaval—volcanic activity, earth shifting, mountain building—as were the other great geologic eras. These convulsions causing drastic changes both terminated species and created an opportunity for the survivors and derivative species to exploit new environments. At first, even as in plant succession, the hardy and opportunistic species with wide tolerances for environmental variations predominated, but gradually gave way under competition from more efficient, specialized forms. However, the specialists were most vulnerable to the suddenly changed environment, and every plant species that faded out of existence probably took with it a constellation of specialized herbivores, predators, and parasites.

The dinosaurs appeared, evolved, and flourished, then declined to extinction during the 130 million years of the

Mesozoic era. Development of the mammals, including primates, began with the Cenozoic 60 million years ago. With the start of the Pleistocene epoch about one or more million years ago, LaMont Cole suggests, "the earth may have entered a new geological revolution. Certainly, mountain-building, vulcanism, and glaciation today are far in excess of the geological norm. But in this particular highly abnormal instant of geological time, a new species, *Homo sapiens*, has risen to prominence."

2

The rise of man had been in the making ever since the formation of the primate order. At one time, some of the genes that were to replicate a human being were shared with tree shrews and a host of other species. But the evolutionary road is a series of forks with each species making a decision, without knowing, of course, whether the path leads to success or extinction. With the division of monkeys and anthropoid apes some 20 to 25 million years ago at about the start of the Miocene epoch, ancestral man became recognizable. The anthropoids are larger in size than monkeys, tailless and characterized by longer parental care for their young and pronounced brain development.

During the Miocene, a change in climate thinned the forests of East Africa, converting them to grasslands with islands of trees. Some bands of the arboreal anthropoids, trapped in isolated and dwindling groves of trees, were forced to take to open country and risk exposure to predators at the forest edge and in the grassland. These anthropoids undoubtedly headed for the next arboreal oasis, and if this were occupied, a fight ensued and the losers were forced to move on.

Unquestionably, many anthropoid species became extinct during this transitional process, but some of them became adapted to terrestrial living. It is interesting to see today the range of habitats for anthropoids. Gibbons and orangutans rarely venture to the ground. Chimpanzees spend much time feeding in trees, but considerable time on the ground as well. Gorillas may feed and roost at night in trees, but are more terrestrial than chimps. Man can still climb trees but spends little time in them.

It appears that human ancestors were separated from the other apes, ironically, because the hominoids were the losers in the fights for the wooded groves; these weaker animals were forced to live in edge country or grasslands, forced to earn their living in new ways, forced to survive or fail in a new habitat. Survival brought structural changes, for behavior and morphology interact, with the most successful changes culled by natural selection. Hominoids probably learned to run on two feet before they could walk, and the novel bipedal method of locomotion, walking, conferred one revolutionary advantage. It freed the hands for carrying things.

These bands of hominoids probably numbered between ten and thirty members, much like today's gorillas. Gorillas generally live in groups of five males and about eight females. The group is led by a silverback (gray-haired) male with a second silverback who yields to the leader but is superior to all others. Dominance hierarchy prevails. Next in authority are the blackback males and the females, all of whom are co-equals. But the females are more equal, in the Orwellian sense, at certain times than at others. A female with young will assume dominance over all males when the occasion arises. On similar human occasions, a sinking ship for instance, women and children take the same precedence

—for the reason that there is where the future of the species lies.

The rule determining when species have differentiated is that point at which members from the two populations no longer can reproduce an offspring. For pongids—the great apes—and hominids, this final parting of the ways came several million years ago in the Pliocene epoch. Ancestral man had been gradually changing because of his life in the savannah; he lost his long canine teeth and his body fur, the pelvis was changing so that he could walk in a more upright posture, he could copulate from a frontal position. But the crucial development along the road to modern man was the discovery and use of "tools."

By the beginning of the Pleistocene which coincides with the Paleolithic or Old Stone Age, hominids were ready to begin their evolution to the first domestic animal: man. Paleontologists believe this development grew out of proto-man's love affair with tools. Even the crudest stone tool confers a tremendous advantage to its user, especially a fangless, clawless creature. Held in the hand, it can be used for pounding, digging, or scraping. Flesh and bone can be cut with a flaked chip while a mild blow with the fist becomes a lethal act when the fist holds a stone. Beyond that, stones can be used to make other tools from stone, and also with a stone tool, wood becomes an accessible material.

The use of tools and then the making of them, the hunting in coordinated groups and the need for language, and the pressures of an ever more complex social life brought about a cultural evolution in hominids . . . and the final biological change. In response to the intricate motor and behavioral demands, the hominid brain began to grow in size. This, in turn, expanded the organism's adaptive capacity. By 500,000 years ago, the species *Homo erectus* emerged. He began using fire, sitting in smoke-filled caves and making his first acquaintance with air pollution. The use of fire, the Promethean gift, was the first human experience with the non-biological release of energy.

The enlarged cranial cavity decreed the birth of young before completion of the central nervous system, caused offspring to be completely dependent at birth, extended the period of dependency, required more intense and longer maternal solicitude with attendant domesticating responsibilities for the father, emphasized the necessity for acquired learning, and reinforced cultural development so that thereafter the species evolved *only* culturally. The birth of immature offspring also may have been what brought about man's hairlessness. Julian Huxley writes, "The distribution of hair on man is extremely similar to that on a late fetus of a chimpanzee, and there can be little doubt that it represents an extension of this temporary anthropoid phase into permanence."

The brain reached its present size about 40,000 years ago. By that time, *Homo sapiens* walked the earth. Intelligent man was bequeathed wood and bone as well as stone tools by his ancestors; also clothing, art, burial customs, religion, and the bow and arrow. These advantages together with his use of fire and his erect bipedal gait equipped him to colonize the planet, which he proceeded to do.

One other hominine species coexisted with *sapiens*, Neanderthal man. The skull of Neanderthal man compares to that of *Homo sapiens* in the same ways that the skull of a wild dog compares to that of a domesticated dog, or a wild rat to a tame rat, wild pig or horse to their domesticated counterparts. In the domesticated varieties, there is a brain and corresponding skull enlargement which diminishes the size of the brows and faces. Neanderthal man disappeared at the end of the last glacial period, just before man's modern story was to begin.

Before Pleistocene, one million, two million, years ago, hominids made their living largely by gathering fruits, berries, roots, and nuts (and probably ate carrion when they could). Gathering is an arduous, time-consuming occupation, geographically restrictive. But with the first technology —tools or weapons—hominids began changing their lifestyle. The prey metamophosed into a predator. The hunters became so good at their occupation that by the time *Homo sapiens* perfected the blade spearhead, man became a big-game hunter. Clovis points—named for their archeological site in New Mexico—were the culmination of Old Stone Age technology. Chipped with great skill, the head possessed a fluted shaft that fitted into a split-spear pole.

Paleoecologist Paul Martin has traced a series of big-game extinctions—giant camels, sloths, rodents—and there is an uncanny correspondence of these disappearances to the estimated migration of *Homo sapiens*. The extinctions began in Africa and Southeast Asia about 50,000 years ago, just about the time *Homo sapiens* became a species. The extinctions spread like man through Asia to Australia about 25,000 years ago. The Clovis technology is believed to have reached the Americas via the land bridge between Siberia and Alaska about 11,000 years ago, at about the time that big-game extinctions were under way in the New World. "The survivors," says Dr. Martin, "deer, antelope, wapiti, musk oxen, caribou, moose, pronghorn, mountain goats, mountain sheep and bison, represent only 30 per cent of the big game fauna present earlier." These big-game extinctions took place on the more remote islands—such as Madagascar, New Zealand, and Cuba—during the most recent times, between 4,000 and 400 years ago. There still may be other explanations for these disappearances, but many authorities now believe man had something to do with them.

Homo sapiens used other methods in mass killing. He could chase and flush game with fire; this required burning down grassland or a woodland area. He also discovered the technique of driving herds over a cliff to destruction below. Within a single layer uncovered at Solutré in France are the remains of more than 100,000 horses. So the list of man-endangered species apparently began long before humans learned to spell the names or write the entries.

We can still see how Stone Age man lived by observing today's vestige populations. Only Eskimos are complete predators, carnivores, although the Masai people of East Africa feed on the meat, milk, and blood of their cattle and so are also exclusively secondary consumers. At the other extreme were the Shoshoni Indians who lived in the Great Basin Desert and were seed and root gatherers, herbivores. Australian aborigines, omnivores, function as primary consumers of a variety of roots, fruits, nuts, and plants; secondary consumers of such herbivores as kangaroos and other marsupials, birds, fish, frogs, lizards, and grubs; and as tertiary consumers of such other carnivores as opossums, seals, iguanas, and snakes.

As a gatherer, man exerted the same slight impact upon natural environment as other herbivore species—affecting the relative abundance of certain plants and competing with other herbivores for food. As a hunter, he began to make his presence felt more appreciably; with fire, he began his first broad-scale alterations of the environment. At the end of the Pleistocene, man was a prime competitor, a first among equals. On the strength of his first revolution, his population represented a 10- or 20-fold increase over the original hominid stocks at the beginning of the Pleistocene.

There were less than five million human beings about 10,000 years ago when *Homo sapiens* reached the threshold of the second revolution.

3

The essence of this revolution consisted in the change from *getting* food to *producing* it—from the unconscious procuring of food to man's conscious manipulation of food supply to his advantage.

Pleistocene hunters had probably domesticated one animal. The golden jackals that scavenged the hunter's leavings gradually assumed an initiative and active cooperation in leading men to prey in return for a share of the kill. Men merely exercised authority in this beneficial arrangement with dogs, an alliance that has lasted until the present despite radically altered circumstances.

But with the domestication of sheep and goats along the steppes of Central Asia, men for the first time completely controlled another species for human advantage. Nomadic pastoralism provided men with milk, meat, and clothing in one operation. But these animals grazed close to the ground and the penalty of remaining in one place too long was destruction of the grassland. This kind of grassland destruction and erosion, caused by overgrazing, was repeated again and again. The lesson had to be learned and relearned. The price for shepherding animals, said Frank Fraser Darling, "is movement, the brand of Ishmael."

Shepherding was a cultural *cul de sac*, but the domestication of plants—agriculture—proved to be an open-ended innovation. For most of his 500,000 years, *Homo* was intimately involved with plants; by the Recent Age, he had accumulated a rich lore of experience with wild wheat, barley, and other food plants. This knowledge resulted in an explosion of food production in a dozen or more sites around a crescent of uplands from Jericho on the Eastern Mediterranean through what is now Turkey and southward into present-day Iraqui Kurdistan flanking the Tigris and Euphrates rivers. Wheat, barley, and other cereal grains were the first domesticated plants. This accomplishment seems to have been followed closely by domestication of many of today's farm animals including goats, sheep, cattle, pigs, horses, asses, and dogs.

As the agricultural revolution spread across the Aegean and up the valleys of the Dneiper and Danube, other aspects of life began to change, too. By 5500 B.C. village-farming communities of from 200 to 500 people were becoming common in parts of Mesopotamia. These villages gradually spread from the hills and piedmont down the two great river valleys. By about 4000 B.C., the first Mesopotamian city-state, Ubaid, had arisen. The records of Jericho are also 6,000 years old. Urbanization had begun. From 3000 B.C. to 2500 B.C., the Sumerian civilization was in full flower.

It can be seen how quickly civilization arose after the cultivation of plants and then the transport and storage of grains. In short order, large groups of humans were able to live together in one place. At the same time, there was a division of labor to exploit new niches created by surplus food, a new leisure, and higher human densities. Non-agricultural products were made, the beginnings of industry. Trade for copper was carried on with Anatolia and Oman more than a thousand miles away. In the later times, royal personages were buried with beautifully wrought weapons and ornaments of gold and lapis lazuli. The city of Urak contained perhaps 50,000 inhabitants. While most adults still worked in primary agricultural production, one temple archive records in a parish of about 1,200 people: 90 herdsmen, 80 soldier-laborers, 100 fishermen, 125 sailors, pilots, and oarsmen, 25 scribes, 25 carpenters, smiths, potters, leather-workers, stonecutters, and basket-weavers, and some 300 slaves.

One of the niches that evolved out of urbanization was that of kings. They made a place for themselves in society out of that characteristic human institution, war.

The growing complexity of pursuits led to series of disputes—between herdsman and farmer, fisherman and sailor, plowmaker and plowman. Institutions in the city arose to mediate these conflicts and early myths had it that the welfare of the city goddess rested upon the harmonious interdependence of the shepherds and farmers.

Border disputes arose between city-states; contests for water rights and access to water for vital irrigation almost certainly were involved in these conflicts. At first, the cities were ruled by an assembly of adult male members of the community. Such bodies usually met only at times of threat to appoint a temporary war leader. Eventually, successful war leaders were retained in times of peace, and another institution was begun: to plan for defensive and offensive wars against neighboring city-states. The war-leaders turned into kings who became preoccupied with the consolidation of power.

When this first urban civilization spread to the alluvial low-lands, it could only keep growing through irrigation. For centuries the land was lush with verdure and colorful with flowers, and the hanging gardens of Babylon became one of the wonders of the world. But men at this stage could hardly be expected to anticipate the insidious transformations that can occur through improper irrigation. Without proper drainage, the water evaporates, leaving a crust of salts that finally becomes too toxic for plant life or else salinization of topsoil can be brought about when the water table rises, bringing with it mineral salt deposits from subterranean layers. Or runoff can deplete the topsoil, usher in erosion, and clog the canals with silt. "These things had to be learned empirically and at great cost," writes LaMont Cole, "for they were probably the principal factors causing the collapse of the great Babylonian Empire and other civilizations of the Middle East and Mediterranean regions."

It is just possible that these new agriculturists may have had an inkling of the problem, for the record in one region shows use of crops with increasing salt tolerance. But even suspecting the problem, the farmers did not know what to do about it. Dogged by necessity, they planted for today and let tomorrow take care of itself.

The impressive but singleminded perspicacity of these early civilizations produced other unlooked-for effects upon the land. Someone discovered that through heat copper could be extracted from ore. Then it was discovered that the soft copper could be alloyed with tin to make bronze; that required more heat. Later, the smelting industry grew with the discovery of iron. These desirable trinkets, commodities, tools, and weapons needed increasing amounts of wood for fire. Men raided the forests. While a forest can return through succession if the ingredients are available, it cannot overcome debased soil.

The Biblical Song of Solomon is testimony to the artistic achievements of the early civilizations. Its poetry extols the beauties of Lebanon in sensitive imagery. The forests of Lebanon were a jewel of the ancient world. The cedars were used to build Solomon's temple and his fleet in the Gulf of Aqaba. From the port of Biblos, cedar wood was exported all over the Mediterranean. Today the Lebanese mountainsides are nearly barren.

On the other side of Asia, China possessed one of the

great deciduous forests. In ancient times the sky over Che-
kiang was black with the smoke from wood-fed kilns making
pottery. For centuries now, China has been plagued by the
soil from denuded hills silting her rivers.

Solomon lived in the tenth century B.C. By the fourth
century B.C., Plato contemplated the deforestation and effects from overgrazing in the Greek countryside and lamented that the lands "resemble the bones of a diseased
body."

The melancholy plot was restaged through time and geography. Spain, sensing that the center of gravity of the
political world rested within its borders in the 16th century,
seized the opportunity to build the great armada and to fuel
the smelting for the cannon and swords, finishing the land
degradation begun by nomadic overgrazing, by cutting her
forests, and Spain subsided from the eminence of Charles V
and Phillip II.

When Europeans reached the virgin forests of North
America, they indulged in an orgy of destruction. When
Stewart Udall was Secretary of the Interior, he described
that destruction in these terms: "There was enough wood
for a thousand years, the optimists said, but the lumbermen
levelled most of the forests in a hundred. The devastation
was not caused by logging alone: careless loggers caused
fires that burned as much as 25 million acres each year.
Some irresponsible lumbermen deliberately set fire to the
debris they left behind, thus destroying seedlings that would
have replenished the ravaged forests."

But men always had been able to move on to some unde-
filed place. The world seemed boundless long after men
discovered it was finite. Men formed other important concepts about the world and their place in it. As they wrestled
free of nature's embrace, they abetted the separation men-
tally.

Not only did *Homo sapiens* enjoy many obvious advantages over competing species, but Western man went on to infer that because he was so favored he must have a supernatural ally. God's gift to man of dominion over the earth and all other life can be regarded as nothing more than a religious reporter's description of the situation that actually existed. The fact is that at the time Genesis was written, *Homo sapiens* was graduating from first among equals to dominant animal species of the planet. A perspicacious mind simply recorded a process still in its early stages.

But once the words were written in holy scripture, "have dominion over" and "subdue" the earth, they became decree, duty, and creed. They sanctioned stripping the rights of nature and all other creatures, which existed at man's sufferance and to serve him.

The historian Lynn White, Jr., says that Saint Francis of Assisi "tried to depose man from his monarchy over creation and set up a democracy of all God's creatures." The 13th-century monk failed and "the prime miracle of Saint Francis," says White, "is the fact that he did not end at the stake."

So attached did the monarchs become to the concept of their divine rights and origins that Darwin's revelations of a common heritage with "beasts" and "animals" were received with anguished shock or rejected with righteous indignation.

Individuality in man was expressed in a way unique in nature . . . through the individual. Civilization enhanced individual qualities. In all other species, while single specimens might excel for longevity or size or comeliness, still, "if you have seen one redwood," as Governor Reagan is reputed to have said, "you've seen them all."

Having relaxed the natural bonds to some degree, the

individual was partially freed from natural or regulated behavior: for example, an animal rarely kills and never en-
slaves a member of its own species. But man could break
the rules: kill his neighbor, take his wife, steal his property,
and enslave his children! The Ten Commandments are un-
necessary in nature and the declaration that life, liberty,
and the pursuit of happiness are unalienable rights simply is
untrue. In a natural system, life might be a privilege, but
everybody exercises the right to have somebody else for
dinner. However, the act of predation, which man has an-
thropomorphically likened to his own ferocious violence, is
different from aggression and performed without anger.

The human being also is freed to appreciate his world, to
have an effect upon it, to contribute, to realize his potential-
ities. The significance of the species' unique position was
grasped in the sentience of the Renaissance when modern
man rubbed his eyes and took a fresh look at the world.
The human position was eloquently stated in a speech on
the dignity of man by a Renaissance humanist, Pico della
Mirandola. Jacob Burckhardt in *The Civilization of the
Renaissance in Italy* writes of the speech:

"God, he tells us, made man at the close of the creation,
to know the laws of the universe, to love its beauty, to
admire its greatness. He bound him to no fixed place, to no
prescribed work, and by no iron necessity, but gave him
freedom to will and to love. 'I have set thee,' says the
Creator to Adam, 'in the midst of the world, that thou
mightest be free to shape and to overcome thyself. Thou
mayst sink into a beast, and be born anew to the divine
likeness. The brutes bring from their mother's body what
they will carry with them as long as they live; the higher
spirits are from the beginning, or soon after, what they will
be for ever. To thee alone is given a growth and a development depending on thine own free will.' "

God was more succinct in Genesis. "Behold, the man is become as one of us, to know good and evil."

4

If the first cultural or tool revolution created man and made him first among equals and the second agricultural or urban revolution elevated him to dominant species on the earth, the third revolution led him to his present station: usurper of the planet.

The first revolution is measured in millions of years, the second in thousands, the third in hundreds. As a result of the first revolution, the human population numbered less than five million. In response to the second revolution, it increased 100 fold during 10,000 years to 500 million people, but its growth rate was leveling off in 1650, an arbitrary date picked for the start of the third revolution.

That revolution is known by several names: Industrial, Scientific, and Technological. But what it was, really, was a revolution in energy.

In the beginning, the proto-human species competed with the others for a share of the contemporary solar energy available as food.

"Between this earliest stage and the dawn of recorded history," writes M. King Hubbert in *Resources and Man*, "this species distinguished itself from all others in its inventiveness of means for the conquest of a larger and larger fraction of the available energy. The invention of clothing, the use of weapons, the control of fire, the domestication of animals and plants, all had this in common: each increased the fraction of solar energy available for use by the human species, thereby upsetting the ecologic balance in favor of an increased population of the human species, forcing adjustments of all other populations of the complex of which the human species was a member."

Hubbert says that a slowly increasing human population generally kept abreast of the gradual increase of energy sources: using wood for heat, tapping water and wind for power, using beasts of burden, and increasing the food supply. "Emancipation from this dependence on contemporary solar energy was not possible until some other and hitherto unknown source of energy should become available." This discovery came during the 12th or 13th century when people living on the northeast coast of England discovered that black rocks—"sea coules," they were called—would burn.

The use of coal developed very slowly for many centuries and only became significant after 1800. Half of the total coal used in the United States has been burned since 1930. With the invention of the steam engine by James Watt in England 200 years ago, the chemical energy from coal could be converted to physical work. The steam engine was followed by the locomotive, steamships, and steam-electric power. Then, a little more than a century ago, a second huge source of fossil energy was discovered in petroleum and natural gas. This led to the internal combustion engine, automobile, airplane, and diesel-electric power. Finally, since World War Two, a third and only non-solar source of energy from the nucleus of the atom has been harnessed for man's use.

Not only had man gone out and subdued the earth—it's estimated that only about one-third of the land surface of the planet still is populated by natural ecosystems—but he was well on the way to freeing himself from God's curse after Eden: "In the sweat of thy face shalt thou eat bread."

Geologist Hubbert says that for the past century energy from fossil fuels has increased at about 4 percent a year; in response, the human population is imcreasing at about 2 percent a year. Where the human energy requirements once were 100 thermal watts a day (the equivalent of 2,000 calories of food), they have ballooned to today's 10,000 thermal watt demand for each person in the United States, 99 percent of it in non-nutritive energy.

Since it took approximately 600 million years to accumulate the coal, oil, and natural gas reserves, they may be considered non-renewable resources for human purposes. With this in mind and the fact that the best scientific estimates are that, at present rates of consumption, the bulk of oil will be exhausted in 70 to 80 years and coal in two or three centuries, knowing that we live on a finite planet and that the law of nature always is ultimate equilibrium, it is striking to hear an adviser to Presidents, Walter Heller, say: "I cannot conceive of a successful economy without growth." And to see that nations are willing—eager—to export their oil or other non-renewable resources. And to realize that manufacturers deliberately plan obsolescence for products in order to consume resources more quickly.

These actions and beliefs are consistent, of course, with economics, the science with the same Greek root as ecology but responsible for contradictory courses of action. "The one important difference between ecological and economic systems," says economist Kenneth Boulding, "is that there seems to be no parallel in ecological systems for the economic concept of money, perhaps because in ecological systems there is no overriding species in the interests of which the value of the system is gauged. Man needs a medium of exchange and a measure of value in the form of money, because he needs to refer the whole system of commodities to his own welfare."

Economist Boulding points to many similarities between the two disciplines. Ecology, he says, is interested in how a species in nature earns its living while economics is concerned with how man earns his living. Both sciences share the concept of population; he has studied the birth rate, growth rate, density, and mortality of a population of automobiles. Organizations with their members or factories also might be considered economic species. Both sciences, Boulding says, have a concept of general equilibrium, a system of exchange among various individuals, imply a concept of development, and finally, both systems are subject to distortion or manipulation, if you prefer, to suit man's purposes. Agriculture represents such a distortion of natural systems. The interventions of social policy—education to encourage knowledgeable citizens, religion to produce moral ones, government to promote national or municipal purposes—are parallels in the economic system.

We see that the law of niche operates in economics with devastating effect. When there is a head-on clash between television and magazines for national advertising revenues, *The Saturday Evening Post* crashes, *Life* and *McCalls* wobble while other magazines turn to specialization for survival. In transportation, the all-or-nothing principle drives passenger railroads off the tracks as air and automobile travel prospers.

Indeed, the basic laws of the market postulated by Adam Smith in his *Wealth of Nations* which in 1776 laid the foundation for economic theory sound like the principles that operate in a natural community. As Robert Heilbroner put it in *The Worldly Philosophers:*

" 'It is not from the benevolence of the butcher, the brewer, or the baker that we expect our dinner,' says Smith, 'but from their regard to their self-interest. We address ourselves not to their humanity, but to their self-love, and never talk to them of our necessities, but of their advantages.'

"But self-interest is only half the picture. It drives men to action. But something else must prevent the pushing of profit-hungry individuals from holding society up to exorbitant ransom: a community activated only by self-interest would be a community of ruthless profiteers. This regulator is competition, the socially beneficial consequence of the conflicting self-interests of all the members of society. For each man, out to do his best for himself with no thought of social cost, is faced with a flock of similarly motivated individuals who are in exactly the same boat. Each is only too eager to take advantage of his neighbor's greed if it urges him to exceed a common denominator of acceptable behavior. A man who permits his self-interest to run away with him will find that competitors have slipped in to take his trade away; if he charges too much for his wares or refuses to pay as much as everybody else for his worker, he will find himself without buyers in the one case and without employees in the other. Thus . . . the selfish motives of men are transmuted by interaction to yield the most unexpected of results: social harmony."

Of course, as economist Boulding indicated, the distortions have grown from Adam Smith's day, economically just as they have ecologically. The market has been pushed and pulled by big industry, big unions, big investors, and various government interventions.

But there is another way in which economic theory distorts ecological reality. Economics is an abstraction and, since men set the values, certain seemingly unimportant items traditionally were left out of the equation. Gross National Product, for example, does not reflect deterioration of environment or depletion of resources. The economically uninitiated might consider this oversight close to the whole ballgame.

In economics, a company's air pollution goes by the euphemism of "external cost," meaning that it is not included in the cost of production. The nearby housewife must spend more money to keep her apartment and clothes clean, her husband must pay more in doctor bills, and the manufacturer saves money on production. It is to industry's advantage, of course, to "externalize" as many of the costs as possible. One of the long, bitter struggles of the Industrial Revolution has been society's effort to force industry to assume the costs of externalities. Garrett Hardin listed some of the important manufacturing costs as an ecologist would view them, noting that at one time they probably all were externalities:

1. Raw materials.
2. Labor.
3. Cost of raising and educating a labor force.
4. Cost of industrial accidents.
5. Cost of industrial disease.
6. Cost of cleaning up pollution of the environment.
7. Cost of preventing pollution of the environment.

A paper mill's externalities upstream can be the fisherman's poison downstream. The result can be cheap paper and expensive fish, or too much paper and not enough fish. If the paper mill were made to bear its true costs, the fishing industry might survive, and the fish, too. If the Federal Government removed the depletion allowance for bauxite, the aluminum industry would be forced to recycle aluminum cans at an enormous saving in electrical power (because of the great heat required to extract the metal from the ore). Thus economics could play a vital role in improving environment if all environmental factors were put into the equation.

"In a managed ecosystem," says biology Professor Edgar Taschdjian, "the channeling of the flow of money is the critical factor which determines the output, the stability and the information content of the system. Whether we decide to spend money on a dam construction, on pest control, on sewage treatment or reforestation will make the difference ... We have the choice and freedom of determining how much money is spent on population control or on pollution control and the allocations we make will determine the evolution of the ecosystem in which we live."

But the question for our times is: Who is minding the ecosystem? No one has to be burdened with this responsibility in the natural ecosystem. As Adam Smith's model based on natural principles showed, the invisible hand of self-interest leads to social harmony. The difference between the natural ecosystem and the human ecosystem is that the principal works effectively in the former.

In gaining freedom from natural regulation, a powerful force was unleashed in the human species, one that has no parallel in nature—egocentrism. One textbook, *Ecology and Field Biology* by Robert L. Smith, devotes a section to egocentric animal behavior—the time the animal spends on maintenance, shelter seeking, escape, and defense. But this is such an insignificant factor in natural ecology that it is not mentioned in less encyclopedic works. While social caste is implied in dominance hierarchy, there are no equivalents for such important human factors as ambition, revenge, *machismo*, narcissism, envy, nepotism, inferiority complex, and many more. There are no strikes in nature, no voluntary non-cooperation, no psychosomatic disruption of patterns. Nor is there intraspecific slavery and exploitation (greed is a human distortion of natural providence). The rising Cost of Living is a national index to the ungovernable force of self-interest. Each person or group acts from self-interest, attempting to gain an advantage, to exact a better relative position, and the result is not social harmony but diluted wealth.

The erosion of the ecosystem can be seen through this disintegrative egocentrism. The automobile is a personal interest solution to transportation. Air conditioning is a personal interest solution to summer heat. As in any comparable ecological situation, impact upon the environment is negligible until the population of autos or air conditioners reaches a certain density. Except that in the human ecosystem, the "tools" run roughshod over environmental resistance, and the environment is degraded. Two nationwide surveys in 1967 asked, "The auto pollutes air, creates traffic, demolishes property, and kills people. Is the contribution the auto makes to our way of life worth this?" Four out of five persons, including those in metropolitan areas, answered yes.

In the case of air conditioners, the electrical energy limits already are being reached in New York City with summer brownouts, foreshadowing the paradox of a day when everyone owns an air conditioner and nobody is able to use it.

Garrett Hardin, in "The Tragedy of the Commons," posed the problem as a pasture shared by a number of herdsmen, each of whom asks himself what is the utility of adding one more animal to his herd. The utility has both a positive component—that he will have one more fatted steer—and a negative component—a slight increase in overgrazing.

But, the herdsman reasons, he will benefit completely from the additional animal whereas the hardly noticeable environmental deterioration will be pro-rated among all users of the commons. "Adding together the component partial utilities, the rational herdsman concludes that the only sensible course for him to pursue is to add another animal to his herd. And another; and another. . . . But this is the conclusion reached by each and every rational herdsman sharing a commons. Therein is the tragedy. Each man is locked into a system that compels him to increase his herd without limit—in a world that is limited. Ruin is the destination toward which all men rush, each pursuing his own best interest in a society that believes in the freedom of the commons."

Hardin said he used the word tragedy in the sense of "the solemnity of the remorseless working of things." From the cedars of Lebanon across 9,000 miles and 3,000 years to the redwoods of California, we can trace "the remorseless working of things." Ecologist David Gates says northern Michigan, where he studied plants as a youth, is "not what it was when I was a boy—nothing is, I guess—but it's still beautiful. It's so difficult to make people understand the seriousness of the threat. They don't realize how much we've lost already. They don't realize that we live in a closed system, that the air and water, the plants and animals, are being irreparably damaged and there are no replacements."

So inexorable is the egocentric working of things, so inextricably locked into the system that two outspoken popular defenders of environment—Arthur Godfrey and Eddie Albert—found that in selling detergents heavily laden with phosphates they were agents in the eutrophication of American waters . . . that some of the nation's most influential law firms work for the most important industrial polluters . . . and that millions of Americans must earn their livelihood by making and servicing and using the environmentally contaminating internal combustion engine. How many men have gone to their graves with personal fortunes leaving the commons a little poorer?

If the binding human rules comparable to the regulations of nature are not be be found in economics, let us look at other civilized institutions. The law evolved out of trial by combat as a method, like social dominance, for reducing violence in disputes. It is in this arena that the force of egocentrism can be contained and where the whole has imposed its will upon the parts. Out of the conflict of individual self-interest against individual self-interest or personal interest versus society's interest has come the human concept of justice.

But humans have not been completely successful in extending enforceable law to regulate the actions of nations. And it is on this level that the egocentric force carries its most dangerous potential. The constant threat of nuclear war poses one of the major methods of planetary destruction. Richard Falk, a professor of international law at Princeton University, sees an equally grave inability to cope with planet-wide environmental problems. If these assaults attain the magnitude to threaten the survival of the human species, Professor Falk says, "no national government, no matter how enlightened it becomes, can expect to handle these problems alone, and that kind of conclusion goes against the whole tradition of international relations where the basic assumption was one of independence rather than interdependence. The prevailing attitudes and structures of international society are based on the faulty assumption that each nation pursuing its own welfare leads to a tolerable total result for mankind as a whole. It is really an invisible hand notion on a national level writ large and applied to the whole of mankind." An unregulated situation in human affairs frequently is referred to as a jungle, but the fact is no such anarchy exists in nature.

Human law has been important or immature when it comes to environmental or interspecific events, for law has concerned itself with interactions among humans. The environment or other species usually have had meaning or rights only in a human context—as property. Now a few pioneering lawyers are grappling with the enormous legal problem of protecting man's environment from man. In this perspective it can be seen that the National Environmental Policy Act of 1969 and such state acts as New York's Conservation Bill of Rights Amendment and Michigan's holding polluters liable to lawsuit are pieces of watershed legislation.

Western religion also has been preoccupied with intraspecific actions or else man's relationship with God. Churches traditionally don't consider within their purview the morality of clubbing seal pups in front of their mothers or factory farming that condemns domesticated creatures to birth-to-death incarceration. In this area, it is an ecologist who raises the ethical question. "We have the power to alter the landscape and to exterminate species of animals and plants that we do not like or that we do not find convenient to our purposes," writes Marston Bates. "But do we have the right?"

The Judaic-Christian God that created man in his image also is responsible for all other creatures. The survival of many species may soon require divine intervention.

"Since the time of our Lord, about 100 animals and the same number of birds have become extinct," Britain's Prince Philip said at the founding of the World Wildlife Fund.

"During the past 150 years the rate of extermination of mammals has increased 55-fold," *Time* Magazine quoted ecologist Lee Talbot of the Smithsonian Institution as saying. "If the killing goes on at this pace, in about 30 years all of the remaining four thousand and 62 species of mammals will be gone."

Roger Revelle, head of the Center for Population Studies at Harvard University, set the same deadline as he contemplated the doubling of the human population. "Continuation of even a one per cent rate of population increase much beyond the year 2000 can only bring disaster, not only to mankind but to all other living creatures." Dr. Revelle recommended a series of requisites to an International Biological Program symposium in London in September, 1969, and concluded: "Above all, we need to preserve diversity."

New York Times Science Editor Walter Sullivan in a column about Pleistocene exterminations asked, "Will ours become a one-crop planet—the single crop being *Homo sapiens*?"

Said benthic ecologist Jack Pearce of the Sandy Hook Marine Laboratory after a long study of pollution in the Atlantic Ocean, "Man is working toward a single species environment—man."

Fantastic and bleak as this eventuality may seem, we may come closer to it than we would believe possible. Because in eliminating competitors, in taking over more of the landscape and resources, which has the effect of removing many more species, *Homo sapiens* simply is doing what comes naturally. Man is obeying the natural law requiring each species to exploit the environment to its best advantage and to outcompete all other species. On a grander scale what is happening is no different from the simple competition the Russian ecologist Gause conducted between the two species of paramecia. As one species gradually gains an advantage—just the slightest leverage—it reproduces more and thus takes more and thus reproduces more until it is the only species left.

But in faithfully carrying out the natural law of exploitation, free man—that is, unregulated, ungoverned man—will certainly degrade and probably ruin the environment for himself as well as for most other species. What he is doing naturally is undoubtedly the most exceptional event in earth's history. "Our choices concern the very survival of the human species itself," says ecologist Pierre Dansereau. "The emotional impact is quite different from that of the extinction of the dodo, the great auk, the passenger pigeon; from the dwindling of the caribou, elk, or bison; from the regression of salmon and trout; from the blight on chestnut and elm!"

If man—like *Acanthaster planci*—is caught in an inexorable process of destroying his own habitat, how can he stop himself?

In November, 1968, Dr. Lynton Caldwell a professor of political science from Indiana University urged university centers for the study of human ecology in the United States and Canada. "The argument is premised on the belief that a major effort in research and education in man-environment relationships has become imperative," said Dr. Caldwell. "It is imperative because the stress of human occupancy upon the biosphere of the earth has reached a critical stage. Although Americans may not be prepared to make the effort, a 'Manhattan Project' for human ecology is as greatly needed now as any military preparation ever was."

Ten universities and the Smithsonian Institution, acting as a consortium, have proposed the creation of a National Institute of Ecology. The Ecological Society of America has begun the feasibility study of such an institute. Dr. Caldwell notes that ecological concepts have not permeated public education, an essential if a democratic society is to make the crucial decisions required for its survival.

"It would be difficult to give you a cursory appraisal of the state of human ecology today," wrote Frederick Sargent, II, Dean of the University of Wisconisn's College of Environmental Science in May, 1970. "For the most part it is more a point of view than a specific area in the educational programs of most institutions."

Not only is there no science of human ecology, but so

complex is the subject that there is no agreement of what it is, or should be. Which is it: the phenomenon of man viewed ecologically or the study of natural systems with special reference to man? Should traditional ecologists be admitted to the discipline? After all, they have spent their careers studying everything *but* man. That makes them strong on environment, but what do they know about the perplexing central subject?

A good number of sciences have been concentrating on man for a long time and, in fact, medical science already has laid claim to the title of human ecology. Medical science does deal with the biological interactions of human and other populations, parasites, disease, natality, mortality, nutrition, and metabolism. But medicine traditionally has been uninterested in man's social, cultural, political, and economic behavior, and—captivated by Pasteur's bacteriological revolution—the turning toward environmental medicine is as recent as the ecologists' concentration on *Homo sapiens.*

Sociology would seem the natural home for human ecology. But while sociologists are expert demographers and deal with populations and units, structure and functionalism, they are ignorant of biology, chemistry, physics—all the exact sciences involving man and his environment. The inexactitude of present-day sociology and its disappointing achievements to date hardly inspire enlarging its responsibilities.

Anthropology? Anthropologists have been looking at man over the course of his singular history and have, in fact, uncovered much of the historical material for ecologists to work with. Certainly, anthropology would seem a likely candidate. But anthropology—like medicine, sociology, economics, political science, social psychology, psychiatry—possesses one impediment to becoming an objective science of man. Economist Kenneth Boulding could have been speaking for all these disciplines when he said, "Economists are irretrievably and irredeemably man-centered."

The question of perspective is no mere quibble. Man was unable to understand the workings of the solar system as long as he considered the earth as its center. Distinguished from all the man-centered human sciences, ecology takes a Copernican view. Man is not the center; the system itself is the framework of reference. The focus is on the biosphere, the ecosystem. With this perspective, one sees relationships invisible to the other disciplines. What is good for the biosphere is good for man, although the reverse is not necessarily true. What hurts the biosphere hurts man.

"The case for ecology as a discipline seems to me to be stronger than for human ecology," said Dr. Caldwell. "Both human ecology and economics are man-centered. In gaining a sharpness of focus and apparent relevance by a concentration upon human behavior, they may hazard the larger relevance that can be obtained by observing man in the larger context of nature."

"There is no human ecology," said Frank Fraser Darling, "only ecology. But in those sciences dealing with man, from political economy to social anthropology and archaeology, there is plenty of room for the ecological slant of mind. Ecological studies," he went on, "are not designed *ad hoc* to solve land-use problems, but to discover truth."

It is only from the perspective of ecology that science has seen and proclaimed imminent peril to the human species. Ecologists compared the similarity of the human growth curve to that of insect populations that do not have sufficient governors and crash. Ecologists know the absolute dependence of human welfare upon the environment and know that degradation of the environment will be followed by degradation of human life.

And now that they have started to look at the last species, *Homo sapiens*, they realize that an ecology of man is needed at once.

"I will suggest the predicament of our society," Cornell ecologist Robert Whitaker told a symposium at Brookhaven National Laboratory in May, 1969. "A system of accelerating growth and increasing complexity is stretching ever tighter its means of organization, while producing social and environmental problems ever more difficult and beyond realistic prospects of solution, while increasing the tensions and frustrations of the human beings who must maintain the organization and try to deal with the problems, while producing increasing numbers who scorn the system and its complexities without a rational sense of the limitations on alternatives, while producing small but increasing numbers of human beings sufficiently damaged as such that they desire the ruin of the society which, for all they can understand, is responsible."

Kenneth Watt, a systems ecologist using the mathematical models of human ecosystems, finds that the baby boom of the late 1940s and 1950s shifts the nation's age distribution and produces "an excessive rate of social change." Adults cannot maintain traditional social and moral values. All the wrong things increase: alcoholism, divorce, drug addiction, crime.

George Woodwell sees alarming signs of our technology out of control. Can this be the logical end of the evolutionary road for tool-using, tool-making, technological man? It is as though the very genius that made him man has created now a population of sorcerer's apprentices who through implacable evolutionary growth and ramification, are doubling every generation, multiplying the information, increasing the complexity, accelerating not only the change but the rate of change—to the point that a son no longer can learn about adult survival from his father. Institutions, like eutrophying lakes, undergo forced aging so that society staggers under the burden of superannuated structures. Obsolescence covers the land like a mold and leaders become intellectually obsolete before they attain power. If this is the case, it is simply a matter of time before men no longer can cope with the human ecosystem.

CHAPTER SEVEN

Civilization's Summit

1

THE METROPOLITAN CITY is the most complex environment man has created. And in certain respects the most vulnerable. A transit or sanitation strike quickly demonstrates just how vulnerable. City arteries are thrombotic with traffic and a water main break produces an embolism. American city governments with their unwieldy mass and turgidity are like beached whales. Inner city chancres erupt and blossom, the efflorescence of a national disease. No one wonders that cities are flash points of riots.

Yet cities are probably the most notable and durable of man's creations. If Neil Armstrong took the last step in tool-using man's million-year odyssey, then cities are fruits of the agricultural revolution. From these nests, men have spun the web of today's global civilization. Repositories and generators of human cultural and intellectual achievements, cities appear to exemplify the ecological correlation between complexity-diversity and stability. Rome has existed for 3,000 years while empires have come and gone. Paris has endured the vicissitudes of Gaul and France for more than two millennia. "London," wrote Frank Fraser Darling and Raymond Dasmann, "has gone steadily forward from being the capital of a Belgic tribe to become a provincial

Roman capital, a Saxon capital, and a Norman one, gradually extending its influence to be the heart of a great empire. That empire has gone, but London remains a growing entity, pulsing with new life and adapting to new situations in the politico-economic environment."

Since cities play such an important role in civilization, since their problems are so urgent, and since they are ecosystems, unquestionably the time has come for an urban ecology.

In the urban ecosystem, the rain falls on the city, but the inhabitants get their drinking water from reservoirs perhaps 100 miles away. While there are plants within the city, a New Yorker gets his lettuce from California, apples from Washington, pork chops from Iowa, and coffee from Brazil. Most other animal species in the city live off what man imports. Boats, planes, trains, trucks, and automobiles link the city with producers all over the world. The city could not survive without these links; unlike the largely self-contained medieval city, the modern metropolitan area is a nexus.

Just as man's goods and water come from outside the city, so his wastes do not fertilize the ground beneath him. Biological wastes are partially broken down, then deposited into a river to carry away. In the case of New York City, the residue sludge has been dumped for 40 years in one area south of Ambrose Light Tower, creating 20 square miles of dead sea outside the port of New York. Industrial wastes also are dumped into rivers. Solid wastes go into landfill or are incinerated into the urban air. Units of the urban population seen one day at Times Square on another may appear in Miami Beach, Saigon, or Rio de Janeiro.

Like a natural ecosystem, a city undergoes ecological succession. It starts when pioneer colonizers—hunters or trappers, for instance—appear at the site. Aside from harvesting animals, they leave little mark on the land. They are followed by grazing or subsistence farmers, either of whom completely change the natural community. Some plant and animal species may be destroyed. Industrialization grows within the hub of the farming area; it is followed by urbanization. Great units of natural landscape with their plant species have been replaced by the permanent climax areas of concrete, asphalt, and steel. Subordinate animal species have changed to mostly Norway rats, mice, some park squirrels, pigeons, starlings, sparrows, cockroaches, silverfish, flies, dogs, cats, and a few exotic pets.

In the initial stages of development, the forest ecosystem offers niches to those inhabitants who are generalized and opportunistic. In primitive societies there is virtually no division of labor except between men and women. But as cities develop, the job-niches ramify and generalists give way to specialists. An English village of 1700 had its baker, its blacksmith, its cobbler; a town had its miller, its brewer, its tanner. But London had thousands of craftsmen, playwrights, journalists, merchants, brokers, clergymen, coachmen and lawmakers, administrators, policemen—the last group indicating that as society grows the need for control grows also.

The country boy looked to the city, with good reason, for more opportunities. In today's modern city, the yellow pages of the Telephone Directory hint at how far the process of specialization has gone.

This process of specialization and technological advance takes a high intraspecific toll. As Darling and Dasmann put it, most people "remain as ecological pioneers—generalists —in a world dominated by complex climax communities and have as little hope for survival as pine seeds shed in the shade of a mature forest. Unlike the pine seeds, however, they will not succumb quietly."

The climax city undergoes further succession as it strives to keep dynamic equilibrium. New York City's Environmental Protection Administrator Jerome Kretchmer has measured the chronological succession of a dying area. After a landlord abandons a property, the tenants remain only for 60 to 90 days. Within six months to a year after the first house is deserted, the remainder of the block is abandoned. During that year, the block decays physically and the final community consists of addicts, derelicts, and winos.

In Chicago, a study has shown the ecological pattern that emerges when blacks move into a white area. White workers leave. Unsatisfied with unskilled blacks, industries move out. Since many blacks have less to spend, many stores also move, leaving their premises to storefront churches. As local jobs decline, blacks must spend more not only for higher rents, but to travel farther to work than whites. And so the deteriorating spiral goes.

The most dramatic development in post-urban ecological succession has been suburbanization. A Gallup Poll taken in February, 1970, found that six out of ten people living in the nation's metropolitan centers would move to less urbanized areas if they could. "Man, by both conscious effort and trial and error," writes ecologist Eugene Odum, "is apparently seeking a balance between the advantages of aggregation on the one hand, and isolation or 'territoriality' on the other. The break-up of cities suggests that aggregation can reach a point beyond which the advantage to the population as a whole declines."

Economist Richard Meier polled a group of students—whom he took to be the taste makers of the 1980s—on where they would like to live if they could afford it. About 70 percent of them chose "the kind of images on the land and on the environment that are equivalent to the dispersed urban, which in the Middle West would be about one thousand persons per square miles, or about one fourth the density of the suburban and one fifth the density of the urban." What was preferred, Dr. Meier said, was "the tidiness of the environment, the wildness, some kind of esthetic combination."

The Greek urban and regional planner Constantinos Doxiadis foresees the entire globe becoming one interlocking world-city. He envisions ecumenopolis—"a gigantic city of superhuman dimensions, made up of small units" (of about 50,000 inhabitants); nature would be "converted into a gigantic network with tentacles penetrating deeply into all parts of the universal city so as to reach every residential area—a system of woodlands transformed into parks, intersected by avenues and gardens, within easy reach of our homes."

"Ecumenopolis," Doxiadis writes, "will be a frightening conurbation, but . . . we have no evidences that enable us to conclude that a better sort of city can be created." Once we become convinced that this world-city is inevitable, he says, the only choice is to build it properly.

That means, for one thing, putting transportation underground. Doxiadis compares transportation in the human ecosystem to the circulatory system in the human body. The analogy is not far-fetched. Before the age of ubiquitous and reliable transportation, it was not uncommon for isolated populations to be decimated by famine when local crops failed. One and a half million Indians starved to death during one period in World War Two, not from lack of food, but because of a breakdown in transportation.

Physicist Edwin Marston calculates that because of rising costs, the necessity to circumvent various obstacles and because of objections by conservationists, we are approaching the point where it is no more expensive to build a mile of railroad tunnel than a mile of surface highway. And from the community's point of view, from benefits to the urban ecosystem, there is no comparison between the two modes of transportation, according to Dr. Marston, who teaches a unique course, "The Physics of Urban and Environmental Problems," at Queens College.

A single lane of city freeway carries a maximum of 3,000 people an hour in autos. Buses can transport 30,000 passengers, railroads 40,000 an hour over a single lane or track. Physicist Marston points out that rails are 100 times more economical in land use, require one-tenth the fuel, and require just a few energy plants whereas millions of auto engines distribute pollution thoroughly over the urban-suburban landscape.

In addition to its other community deficits, Dr. Marston teaches that the automobile kills a great many people, presents a solid waste problem, poses a resource problem because it is voraciously consuming petroleum, disrupts cities, is ultimately responsible for oil spills, and causes air pollution.

"It is ironic," he wrote, "that Governor Rockefeller declared war on pollution a few days after he agreed to a subway and bus fare increase. The fare increase will divert travelers from mass transit to taxis and private automobiles and this diversion will probably add an additional 15 million pounds of pollution to New York City's air every year."

Dr. Marston calculates that the typical auto emits one pound of pollution for every 10 miles traveled and the public transit fare increase would shift 100 million riders to autos each year. On the other hand, he says, if the roads were removed from Manhattan's waterfront, many residents would choose to enjoy the improved local environment on weekends and not flee from the city in their cars. With fewer cars on the road, there would be less pollution. The

improved air quality might seduce more stay-at-homes. . . .
Who knows where such a spiral would end?

The development of automobile travel is a classic paradigm of ecological surprises. Henry Ford mass-produced the Model T and America got smog, urban sprawl, and supermarkets.

Communications represents another urban network that has no direct counterpart in the natural ecosystem. The flow of energy, moisture, and nutrients serves to inform the natural community on how well or poorly it is doing. As the niches proliferate and food web ramifies, there are more routes for information, more feedbacks for homeostasis (the self-corrective process). "In terms of "information theory," Dr. Odum wrote in discussing ecological succession, "the total information in the community increases, which means that the number of possible interactions between species, individuals, and materials increases." If the health and well-being of the human ecosystem are regulated by communications governors and feedbacks, freedom of the press can be seen not as a political ideal but as an essential method for maintaining the viability of society.

2

Emanuel Savas, First Deputy City Administrator of New York City, has enumerated other information sources used by the mayor in the cybernetics of city government. These are personal observation, information from subordinates, information from community leaders and other public officials, and information from the public itself. Savas lists four public subgroups—highly vociferous individuals, special-interest groups, civil disorders, and, finally, elections. Each of these information inputs must be judged on a signal (sound with message)-to-noise (sound without message) ratio for the city administration to take proper action.

And even then, Savas notes, "It is difficult to keep a large, sophisticated controller tuned up and functioning well, for there are always component failures, gear slippages, time lags, loose connections, nonlinear effects, and other problems. In government, as in other large organizations, the analogous shortcomings are incompetent individuals in key posts, poor coordination, bureaucratic delays, bad communications, and conventional responses to unconventional situations."

So complex is the urban system, concludes Jay Forrester, a professor of management at Massachusetts Institute of Technology, that it is *counterintuitive*. "Complex systems," he says, "respond to policy changes in directions opposite to what most people expect. We develop experience and intuition almost entirely from contact with simple systems, where cause and effect are closely related in space and time. Complex systems behave very differently."

Savas gives an example of counterintuitive behavior in New York City government. The city has a long, elaborate procedure to protect against graft and corruption in contracting for supplies and services. But there are such delays in securing bids and paying bills that many potential vendors refuse to sell to the city and those who do sell charge higher prices to compensate for the delays. "Thus," Savas concludes, "a strategy designed to increase competition and reduce the cost of goods has the perverse effect of reducing competition and increasing the cost of goods."

Professor Forrester studied a hypothetical city with a systems analysis model that took into account dozens of interacting factors such as new enterprise, mature business, jobs for unemployed, tax collections, public expenditures, and so forth. He presented the computerized results in a book, *Urban Dynamics.*

Professor Forrester found that "Complex systems actively resist most policy changes. A new policy warps the entire system slightly . . . But influence points exist, often where least expected and often with a direction of influence opposite to that anticipated."

That sounds uncommonly close to an assessment by ecologist Crawford Holling: "Natural systems are profoundly resistant to change. They were exposed to catastrophes, natural catastrophes, long before man appeared on the scene; and in order to survive these catastrophes, they developed mechanisms to stabilize their population or their community. But we do know that this resistance isn't infinite; that we can turn a forest into a desert."

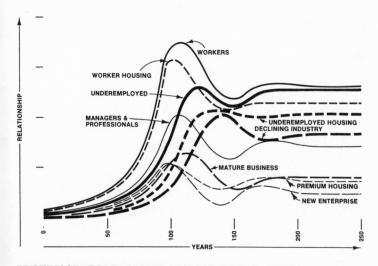

PROFESSOR FORRESTER'S HYPOTHETICAL CITY

Reprinted from *Urban Dynamics* by Jay W. Forrester by permission of The M.I.T. Press, Cambridge, Mass. Coypright © 1969 by The Massachusetts Institute of Technology.

"In a complex system," says Dr. Forrester, "the short-term response to a policy change is often opposite to the long-term effect. This treacherous behavior beguiles the executive and the politician into a series of steps, each appearing beneficial and each leading to deep long-term difficulty."

The use of DDT illustrates this policy in natural systems. The long-lived insecticide at first kills appreciable amounts of target victims. But it also kills their predators. The target pests invariably multiply more quickly than their predators and develop resistant strains more readily. The ultimate result of this policy is more pests, fewer natural restraints, and a poisoned countryside.

What is perhaps most striking about Professor Forrester's city is that it follows a growth pattern uncannily like that of the forest ecosystem. During the first 100 years of its life cycle, it follows the exponential growth pattern, then develops the sigmoidal S, falling where various components have overshot the upper asymptote. The second century is a period of maturing and internal readjustment, and after 200 years there is a continuing equilibrium.

Ecologist Holling has listed four basic similarities between ecological and social systems. The first corresponds exactly with Dr. Forrester's primary finding: both systems have a large number of components and interact in a variety of complex ways. "It is this interaction," says Dr. Holling, "that makes it so dangerous, if easier, to take a fragmental view; to study an isolated piece of any ecological or social system. In concentrating on one fragment and trying to optimize it, we find, to our surprise, that the rest of the system can respond in unsuspected ways." Build a highway system to move people rapidly between cities and the cities are eroded by urban sprawl. Institute a welfare program, you get a backlash. Institute exact fares on buses to curtail robberies, holdups of taxi drivers increase.

Professor Holling also says that the historical character is important to how either system operates, so are the spatial attributes and, finally, there are a variety of structural properties. "Thresholds, for example, are common. The ecologist can show that a predator attacks only when its hunger exceeds a certain threshold. Similarly, the economist's concept of disbursable income argues that people begin to do something different once their income rises above a certain minimum threshold." To illustrate his point further, the University of British Columbia ecologist has written a detailed study comparing predation with land acquisition.

3

Ecologist Kenneth Watt told Congress, "Misuse of land caused by land speculation is one of the great enemies of organized society, and must be regarded as such. A punitive capital gains tax on speculation in land would insure that enough farmland was left under cultivation so that Americans could eat in the future, and have adequate supplies of timber, pulp for paper, and recreational land."

The champion of applying ecological sense to use of land is an acerbic Scotsman who teaches landscape architecture at the University of Pennsylvania and practices what he teaches with his own planning firm. Accompanying these activities, Ian McHarg crusades against the arrogant belief that people can do anything they want to land and get away with it or, in his words, "Man is a blind, witless, low brow, anthropocentric clod who inflicts lesions upon the earth."

McHarg's thesis, contained in the title of his book, is

Design With Nature. When a hurricane struck the New Jersey coast in 1962, more than 10,000 seashore homes were damaged or destroyed. But the storm wasn't the cause of the disaster, only the instrument. Because of overdevelopment, McHarg says, vital ground water was depleted, killing the dune grass that had anchored the beaches. The flood plain, said Aldo Leopold, viewing misplaced construction in the Midwest, belongs to the river.

In providing a rare gleam of leadership in the morass of proper land use, McHarg has planned for the orderly development of 44,000 acres of farms and country estates just northwest of Baltimore. The houses and other structures will be concentrated on hills and plateaus while the valleys will remain untrammelled. The plan opens the area to 83,000 new residents by 1990.

In a land use study of Staten Island—a corner of New York City that somehow eluded the urban homogenization of progress—McHarg carefully mapped the island's hydrology, soil drainage environments, scenic value, historic features value, existing forest quality, suitable urban areas, and other characteristics. The result was a composite gradient map that showed the intrinsic suitability of the land for conservation, urbanization, and recreation or for multiple uses of the three.

The orginality of this approach, McHarg says, consists in its being rational and explicit. The evidence is derived from exact sciences: geology, hydrology, soils, plant ecology, and wildlife. And any other person, accepting the evidence, is likely to reach similar conclusions. "This is in direct contrast to the bulk of planning, where the criteria are often obscure and covert. Moreover, this method permits a most important improvement in planning method—that is, that the community can employ its own value system. Those areas, places, buildings, or spaces that it cherishes can be so identified and incorporated into the value system of the method. Today many planning processes, notably highway planning, are unable to incorporate the value system of the community to be transected. At best, the planner supplies his own distant judgment."

Another way of looking at area or space, as ecologists do, is in proportion to the number of organisms contained in them—the density of population. The die-off of the Sika deer on St. James Island from adrenal malfunctions and other studies of similar phenomena have demonstrated a correspondence of overcrowding to population control. John Calhoun, in a series of famous experiments, found that overcrowding produced a variety of abnormal behavior in laboratory rats—homosexuality, sexual perversions, cannibalism, maternal delinquency, catatonic states—in general, unratlike activities.

Some people were quick to apply the findings to the human situation. But findings by Alexander Kessler and Konrad Lorenz indicated that rats could get along well or at least not exhibit antisocial behavior under conditions of high density as long as they are all known to one another and bear the appropriate smell of friends and relations.

4

With humans, overcrowding is far more complicated than simple density of population. Consider, for instance, the enormous spread in urban densities. In a new city like Houston, the density is less than 3,000 people per square mile; in an old one like Boston it is 14,000 per square mile. The borough of Manhattan is the most densely populated territory in the United States, with 75,000 persons to a square mile and many times that number in certain sections because of temporary business and tourist populations. Manhattan is the likely example when an American considers the social and psychological ills associated with overcrowding. Yet in one 4-acre part of Hong Kong—a city of noted civil order—the density is 2,800 persons per acre, or 1,800,000 people per square mile! Tokyo and Japan are ultra-crowded compared to New York City and America, but the Japanese for centuries have learned how to live with little space by taking little space.

"Most ecologists know," writes George Woodwell, "that the packing problem is not simply a problem of human numbers; it is also a problem of size: people who have developed industrial technology take up more space, use more resources, have more opportunities to interfere with one another and require more rules to fit them into their environment. Most ecologists would also agree that the world could not support even its present three and one-half billions if all nations possessed Western technology and used it with the same lack of controls as we of the West now do."

Each American, with his 500 energy "slaves," is sheathed in a nimbus of energy and mass and throwing off paper, plastics, ash, soot, fumes, and chemical wastes far exceeding his own biological size and wastes. In New York City, where this energy-mass-pollution is concentrated, a distinguished scientist in the field of public health—René Dubos, who heads the department of environmental biomedicine at Rockefeller University—believes that the New York metropolitan area has become an unhealthy place in which to raise children. Dr. Dubos bases this belief upon the spectrum of deleterious environmental conditions that now confront the young human organism. His studies convince him that it is the young organism that is least resistant to harmful environment. What will be the chronic lifetime effects, he wonders, of breathing air so contaminated that no one even knows what constitutes 75 percent of the particulate pollutants? He suspects that a good part of the unknown matter consists of rubber and asbestos particles from auto tires and brake linings—particles that once inhaled never leave the lungs. Similarly, he deplores toxic additives in foods, chemicals in water, the barrage of noise, omnipresence of automobiles, relentless staccato of stimuli and impoverishment of the cityscape.

"An increasingly large percentage of the children in this city live in what I consider a very narrow environment even though they are in the midst of richness. One needs only to walk by some of the housing developments to see how limited the range of visual and emotional stimuli. There may be violent stimuli, but not a very great variety of emotional or intellectual stimuli. And certainly a very great poverty of visual stimuli.

"I am impressed by the fact that most children to whom I have talked in New York City are not aware that there is such a thing as the Milky Way. They have never seen it.

"I live in a new apartment house in one of the best parts of the city and I walk down and there it is—the street is full of junk. And hardly anybody sees it. If a child is raised from the beginning of his life in an environment in which dirt, sloppiness, disorder is the prevailing condition, then this child comes to take this kind of environment as normal."

Dr. Dubos frequently invokes the acuity of Winston Churchill's remark, "We shape our buildings, and afterwards our buildings shape us."

We mold our environment and then it molds us. We pollute our environment today, tomorrow the environment pollutes our children.

CHAPTER EIGHT

Symptoms

1

THE LATEST MASS DISCOVERY of modern man is environment.

The ingredients are obvious enough, being inescapable. And the concept is venerable enough, going back to the first scientist, Hippocrates, who taught not only that environment profoundly influenced health and disease but other human matters as well. Rough countries with excessive seasonal changes, Hippocrates maintained, endowed their inhabitants with strength and violent passions. The despotic political regimes of Asia suppressed men's physical vigor so that they were less effective in war than the Greeks who lived in freedom and democracy.

The force of environment upon men's lives has been depicted frequently enough in literature. *How Green Was My Valley* is a beautifully written tale of a slag hill that grows like an incubus on the Welsh countryside, crushing the inhabitants spiritually. But the British government could see no lesson in the novel's truth and acted only after the children of a village were buried physically under such a slag heap a generation later at Aberfan, Wales.

As touching as the novel was, how could it have universal significance among humans who did not have to live in the demeaning environment of a Welsh mining community? Twenty years ago *How Green Was My Valley* was termed a novel of environment or "local color" and filed away in that category. That's how we dealt with environment then—cerebrally. "Twenty years ago," said Lee duBridge, then Presidential Science Adviser, "the term 'environment' was relatively unused. It was often linked with the word 'heredity' in discussions as to which of these factors was more important in the development of an individual—whether he became a great genius, an ordinary citizen or just a bum."

Today, environment is understood to be the total ambience surrounding the individual or population. It is impossible to conceive of an individual without an environment. Environment includes the air, land, water, trees, buildings; it includes fellow humans, what they say, what they do, what they think; it is history, what the individual thinks, imagines, conceives himself and his world to be. The obscuring of the Milky Way by air pollution reduces the emotional and mental as well as the material environment of the city child. "Fresh" air is invigorating psychologically as well as physically. But environment should not be thought of as a container; it is process, and is affected by every act of every organism.

The interactions of the individual and environment are so intimate—his effects upon it, its effects upon him—that it becomes difficult to distinguish where one leaves off and the other begins. The air we breathe out is not the same as the air we take in. The oxygen in the air one moment is part of a human bloodstream the next. As the science of ecology shows, a human being or a dog or a tree is a temporary arrangement of atoms of minerals, molecules of water, compounds of carbon that at another time may be found in an inorganic gaseous, liquid, or solid condition. The line in

Genesis, "Dust thou art, and unto dust shalt thou return" can be seen to be a prescient statement of reality.

Because of the interchangeability in biogeochemical cycles, *Homo sapiens* carries strontium-90 in his bones, lead in his blood, DDT in his fat, his lungs are black from soot and flecks of asbestos are lodged in the tissue. So far, environmental hazards have merely shortened individual lives, although Thalidomide was a warning that the potential exists for damage to the species itself. LaMont Cole mentions tritium, a radioactive isotope of hydrogen that is given off by nuclear fission reactions and in great quantity by thermonuclear fusion. Tritium is readily incorporated into water molecules and can get into animals and nucleic acids. DNA, the genetic coding for the transmission of life, is held together by hydrogen bonding. But what happens to the genetic message, Cole asks, if the hydrogen is replaced by tritium which changes to helium? Do we start replicating a race of freaks?

The modern concept of environment—as an all-embracing, pervasive matrix in which we live—entered into men's minds only after the prior perception that things were going wrong with it and the dawning realization that these events no longer were isolated in space and time. They were everywhere and were not about to stop and go away by themselves.

That men's recognition of the concomitants of technology was slow and piecemeal is understandable. The consequence escaped even the remarkable clairvoyance of H. G. Wells. In 1913, Wells gave an uncanny preview of major developments of the 20th century in *World Set Free*. The visionary book forecast that men unlocked the secrets of the atom and first used the achievement in a destructive way, dropping atomic bombs in a world war at mid-century. After the holocaust, men turned to peaceful uses of atomic energy and the power set humans free from grubbing for energy. Wells correctly predicted that social organization would lag dangerously behind technological advancement and that laws and courts could not cope well with new problems, as we have seen in environmental matters.

"From the first they (the new world government) had to see the round globe as one problem; it was impossible any longer to deal with it piece by piece." He also wrote: "Men spread now, with the whole power of the race to aid them, into every available region of the earth."

There was one major omission in Wells's vision: he did not foresee pollution.

2

As it turned out, the first pollutions were seen as discrete phenomena. There were radiation pollution, air pollution, water pollution. But the inventory kept growing: pesticide pollution, noise pollution, solid waste pollution, land pollution, thermal pollution, visual pollution, litter, marine pollution, eutrophication. The pollutions began to overlap. Then men began to see that various pollutions could be merely different manifestations of the same problem: if an industrial waste were incinerated, it became air pollution; if dumped into a river, water pollution; if dumped on land, solid waste pollution. Or, looked at another way, the impact of one "tool"—the automobile—upon environment was protean: asbestos particles from the brake lining, rubber particles from the tires, oxides of nitrogen and carbon, oxidents and hydrocarbons from the exhaust, lead from the gasoline—all various forms of air pollution; thermal pollution from the engine; noise pollution from the engine, tires, and horn; water pollution from the nitrogen fumes that settled into lakes and rivers; and a mammoth solid waste problem at the end of the car's usefulness; visual pollution from billboards, signs, and gas stations; land pollution or destruction of green areas for highways and parking aprons.

About 60 percent of the 142 million tons of pollutants released into the American atmosphere each year comes from automobiles. Carbon monoxide, produced almost entirely by autos, composes more than half of all air pollution. Hydrocarbons and nitrogen oxide, also auto by-products, account for nearly another quarter. Sulfur oxide from the combustion of fossil fuels in electric power plants contributes 18 percent of the pollutants, and particulate matter makes up the remaining 9 percent.

Los Angelenos drive around in nearly 9,000 tons of carbon monoxide a day, nearly 1,200 tons of hydrocarbons, 330 tons of oxides of nitrogen, and a sizable tonnage of aldehydes, sulfur compounds, acids, ammonia, lead, and other poisonous substances. According to the Surgeon General's report containing these figures, 80 percent of the pollutants in Los Angeles smog are products of the city's three million privately owned automobiles.

Impressive as these figures are, the fact is that nature produces a far greater volume of many "pollutants"—10 trillion tons of carbon dioxide, for example, compared to 13 billion tons produced by man; nearly 10 times as many oxides of nitrogen and nearly six times as many hydrocarbons. However, very little sulfur dioxide is produced naturally compared to the 146 million tons made by fossil-fuel fires a year, and only one-twentieth the amount of carbon monoxide is caused by forest fires.

A study by Elmer Robinson and Robert Robbins of the Stanford Reserach Institute found that there are very efficient natural mechanisms for disposing of these pollutants, that oxides of nitrogen are removed from the atmosphere within five days, sulfur dioxide in four days; but carbon dioxide stays in the atmosphere for four years, hydrocarbons for sixteen years. These are all part of the biogeochemical recycling process.

The question then becomes, if these substances are produced naturally, is nature a polluter? Or, to put it another way, why isn't nature a polluter? Or, when does pollution occur, what *is* pollution anyway?

Dr. Robbins pointed to the answer when he said that the reason the city dweller is aware of air pollution is that man is adding the offending materials too quickly in urban areas, overloading the natural systems of that sector. "The natural scavenging processes just can't keep up," he said. These substances produced naturally are distributed over wide expanses and the rate of emission is more evenly paced.

"Environmental pollution," the President's Science Advisory Committee said in its 1965 report "Restoring the Quality of Our Environment," "is the unfavorable alteration of our surroundings, wholly or largely as a by-product of man's actions, through direct or indirect effects or changes in energy patterns, radiation levels, chemical and physical constitution and abundances of organisms."

It could be argued that man is a part of nature and, furthermore, it is part of his own nature to be a social and cultural animal. Therefore, his by-products are the result of the natural system that produced him. After all, by simply breathing out, he produces carbon dioxide and it would not be desirable for him to stop even if he could. Similarly, most of the other by-products are associated with such life processes as producing crops for food, warming his home, fueling his transport, clothing his body. For as long as man exists now on this planet, he will always produce by-products.

But these processes are irrelevant to pollution—they may or may not produce pollution. The criterion for pollution is the kind and the amount of the substances sent into natural systems. If the materials can be readily recycled, degraded to original constituents, and absorbed into the process without interfering with the system or without altering the dynamics of the ecosystem, then the by-products can be considered non-polluting. If the material is not adapted to the natural system or provides an unaccustomed stimulus or "insult," then it is a pollutant—a resource out of place in the closed system, as the Committee on Pollution of the National Academy of Science put it.

Pollution and reactions to it are symptoms that natural systems are overstressed, that the biosphere is in trouble.

"It is unbelievable to a layman to recognize that our technology in the United States, the most advanced country in the world, has not been brought to bear on the basic cause of air pollution," says Harold Koenig, president of Ecological Science Corporation, an engineering firm involved with pollution abatement. "What is the primary cause? Real simple. Incomplete products of combustion. Why? Look at the basic burner technology. You mix air with the fuel. Look how it's mixed. There have been no pioneering advances in that basic starting point in, I don't know, a hundred years.

"Anytime you burn, you've got products of oxygen and nitrogen coming out in that exhaust gas because you are burning air. Why hasn't any significant effort been applied to figuring out how to achieve desirable combinations of oxygen and nitrogen coming from the exhaust gas? I think the answer is very simple. Nobody has given a good goddam about the impact on the ecological balance where this discharge is going to be received."

In June, 1970, fifteen New York City medical teams

tested 435 children in a small area of the East Bronx for lead poisoning. Nearly 10 percent of the children tested— 40 of them—were suffering from lead poisoning which is contracted by eating chips of lead-based paint found in old tenements. Increasing levels of the ingested lead can cause severe brain damage and death. "There are 250,000 cases of lead poisoning a year in urban areas," says Glenn Paulson, a biologist and leader of the New York Scientists' Committee for Public Information. "This is a case of an earlier technology whose consequences were completely unknown. No one thought to test the paint for toxicity."

3

Research in the multi-billion dollar detergent industry did not extend to learning about the product's injurious impact upon environment. The result was, first, a detergent that was impervious to the decomposers, so that detergent foamed out of kitchen faucets and over village streams. About a decade after detergents were made biodegradable, they were found to be major contributors to eutrophication of American waterways because they contained phosphate.

The phosphate enriches the lake or stream. In fact, our first knowledge of eutrophication came from efforts to increase the production of fish ponds through adding nutrients. However, while production of fish increases, the species change to less desirable ones. And that's what happens with cultural—man-made—eutrophication. There still is some question whether man-made eutrophication exactly parallels natural maturation, but the processes certainly are similar.

The artificially deposited phosphates, along with nitrates from sewage and farm fertilizers, provide rich food for bacteria and algae, which multiply. The bacteria provide more carbon dioxide for water plants, which increase, providing more oxygen for more bacteria. But the growth of algae and plants chokes the open water and cuts sunlight to the deeper layers of the lake. This kills plant life and thus reduces the oxygen supply. The die-off of excess algae consumes more oxygen in the decaying process. As the oxygen saturation dwindles the fish disappear. Bacteria that do not require oxygen take over the decomposing and the end products of this anaerobic process are foul-smelling hydrogen sulfide, non-potable water that looks like pea-green soup, and the possibility that decaying bottom material is poisoned with botulin toxin.

So the environmental price for clean sheets with the present detergent technology is filthy waterways.

But there are grounds for optimism. With the diversion of sewage from Lake Washington in Seattle, cultural eutrophication not only was stemmed but the process actually reversed. Whether the far more complex natural aging of a body of water can be reversed is another question.

"That we have as yet no practical methods for bringing about an effective slowing down or reversal of that aging process is perhaps disappointing and definitely alarming," wrote Paul Erickson and John Reynolds in a study of the ecology of Quabbin Reservoir in Massachusetts, "but it should not be surprising. We have crawled out from our caves to add cruelly to the burden of an ecological system geared to its own cleansing before we have fully understood the basic microbiological processes by which that cleansing is carried on. If we are now to keep our reservoirs alive we must inquire before we can hope to dictate: we must understand natural mechanisms precisely before we can manipulate them according to our own human requirements."

Until this last moment of the Industrial era, the unlooked-for, unintended, or unwanted environmental effects of technology simply were ignored. They didn't count. They were outside the technological or economic framework. When these effects spread with increasing technology and could no longer be dismissed, they were called side-effects. This served to acknowledge their existence but subordinate them to second-class effects, unimportant effects. But, as Garrett Hardin points out, effects are effects.

4

This belated understanding that the entire spectrum of effects—harmful as well as beneficial—must be weighed heralds the end of the unbridled technological era as we have known it. Moreover, environmental effects—pollution —appear to pose the major limiting factor to man's quest for unlimited energy. While knowledgeable persons talked about electrical energy demands doubling every ten years, New York City began experiencing brownouts in the summer of 1969. With citizen resistance to power plants already high because of environmental pollution, a report published in May, 1970, by the National Research Council-National Academy of Engineering warned that sulfur dioxide pollution from coal and oil-fired electric plants could more than triple by the year 2000. The report said, "Contrary to widely held belief, commercially proven technology for control of sulfur oxides from combustion processes does not exist." The only way now available to reduce SO_2 pollution is to burn low-sulfur fuels, and their supply is limited.

According to the second law of thermodynamics, whenever energy is transferred some of it is lost as heat. Whenever electric power is generated, heat is a by-product. In the production of hydroelectric power, this by-product is negligible. But heat is an integral part of the production of electricity in fossil fuel or nuclear power plants. Water is heated to form steam that passes through turbine blades; the turbine turns a generator that converts mechanical energy into electrical energy.

A nuclear plant has an efficiency of about 30 percent, a fossil fuel plant an efficiency of about 40 percent. This means that for each ten units of heat generated, three units in the case of nuclear plants and four in the case of fossil fuel plants go to produce electricity. The remainder of the heat is waste by-product. If no use is found for this heat—and so far men have not been very successful in conserving or in channeling this heat-energy for constructive purposes—still it must be gotten rid of somehow. A fossil plant discharges some of this heat into the surrounding air and the rest into an adjacent body of water, but the relatively more waste heat from nuclear plants all goes into water unless coolant towers are built.

This unwanted heat has come to be known as thermal pollution. While it is mainly associated with water, anyone who has walked on a summer day along a city street receiving the thermal effluent from air conditioners and automobiles knows that it can change the quality of air as well.

The addition of unwanted heat to living bodies of water can be a limiting factor for fish—trout, particularly, must have cool water. For animals it does not kill outright, the heat may cause them to be more susceptible to chemical toxins or disease pathogens and further weakens their ability to survive by depleting oxygen dissolved in the water. Whereas the aquatic organism might withstand any of these assaults individually, together even in seemingly innocuous amounts they may do the animal in. Investigators became aware of the lethal force of the synergistic effect—that is, a total effect greater than the sum of the effects taken independently—as they began looking at the broad spectrum of the technological barrage against environment. However, Aesop described the phenomenon in his fable of the last straw.

Too much heat also can be a limiting factor for the human species. LaMont Cole says, "With electric power doubling every 10 years, I have calculated that if heat continues to increase at the present rate of seven per cent a year, we will be unable to survive in 130 years. The earth will be uninhabitable."

At least one other limiting factor should intercept that ultimate barrier. Predictions are that by the year 2000, one-half or more of the electric energy in the United States will be produced by nuclear power plants. By that time these nuclear and fossil fuel plants will require water for cooling equal to two-thirds of the average daily run-off of one trillion two hundred billion gallons of all American rivers, and that demand actually would exceed the water supply in non-flood seasons.

5

Radiation impact upon the environment will increase with the enlarged use of atomic energy. Dean Abrahamson, president of the Minnesota Committee for Environmental Information and an officer of the Scientists' Institute for Public Information, writes that by the year 2000 nuclear and fuel processing facilities will be producing 470 million curies of krypton-85 annually. "This represents an increase in radiation exposure of about two millirems per year, or between one and two per cent of the natural background radiation. Other long-lived radionuclides, particularly tritium, will make their own contribution to radiation exposure. In 30 years, radiation levels may be high enough to cause serious and unforeseeable effects on the world's living things, including man, unless technology to control radioactive effluents is developed."

Studies by John Gofman and Arthur Tamplin of the Lawrence Radiation Laboratory in California indicated to them that current permissable radiation standards may not be stringent enough . . . that if 200 million Americans actually were subjected to the maximum allowable radiation dosage, there would be an increase of 24,000 cases of cancer and leukemia per year. This has stimulated scientific controversy, because the Gofman-Tamplin conclusions are virtually impossible to prove or to disprove. But the Federal Radiation Council, which sets the standards, agrees that it is better to err on the side of prudence and undertook a review of the entire area.

The storage of radioactive wastes is an associated problem. Eugene Odum wrote in *Fundamentals of Ecology* in 1959 when atomic weapons still were being tested in the atmosphere, "Although fallout problems are presently in the public eye, waste disposal from peaceful uses of atomic energy is potentially a far greater problem, assuming again that we do not have an all-out atomic war. Not enough attention is now being given to the ecological aspects of waste disposal, which could be the limiting factors to full exploitation of atomic energy."

Seven years later, a Committee on the Geologic Aspects of Radioactive Waste Disposal established by the National Academy of Sciences–National Research Council criticized the Atomic Energy Commission's waste program, saying, "the current practices of disposing of intermediate and low-level liquid wastes and all manner of solid wastes directly into the ground above or in the fresh water zones, although momentarily safe, will lead in the long run to a serious fouling of man's environment."

The first principle set up by this committee was that all radioactive materials are biologically injurious and therefore should be isolated from the biological environment for their periods of harmfulness. The Health Physics Division of the AEC has set this figure at 20 half-lives (that is, the time it takes for a given amount of material to lose half its radioactivity), so that strontium-90 and cesium-137, the by-products of atomic fission with half-lives of 28 years and 30 years, would have to be isolated for 600 years and possibly a millennium. These persistent radioactive materials are sealed away in storage containers, but who can guarantee that a tank will last a thousand years? Research is being conducted on turning these radioactive materials into glass or ceramic slugs to be buried in natural salt beds or concrete-and-metal bins.

The scientists' committee had another worry—"the working philosophy of certain operators, although certainly not that of AEC, that safety and economy are factors of equal weight in radioactive waste disposal." In other words, the limiting factor could be not technology, but human negligence.

In order to make use of ample cooling water, nuclear power plants are planned for bays or ocean coastlines, but some scientists already are alarmed by oceanic pollution. Since 1952, low-level radioactive wastes have been discharged into the Irish Sea from the Windscale nuclear power station on the British coast. Russian scientist G. G. Polikarpov has found radioactivity in the Irish Sea sufficiently high to cause embryo fishes to develop deformed backbones. Dr. Polikarpov and other Soviet investigators have found strontium-90 levels in pelagic eggs of Black Sea anchovies close to maximum permissable levels. On the basis of his investigations, Dr. Polikarpov believes "further radioactive contamination of the seas and oceans is inadmissable."

Nuclear contamination also can enter the oceans by leaks and discharges from atomic submarines. A particularly large amount may have been spread by the sinking of the U.S. nuclear submarine *Thresher* in the North Atlantic in April, 1963. Jerold Lowenstein of the University of California Medical Center, a specialist in nuclear medicine, says the likelihood of a nuclear ship disaster will increase with the growing world fleet of atomic-powered vessels. As it is, Dr. Lowenstein says, "every living thing on and under the sea is being poisoned with radioactive wastes."

Environmental pollution may be the limiting factor even if controlled nuclear fusion is achieved. D. G. Jacobs of the AEC's Health Physics Division says, "The amount of tritium produced in thermonuclear reactions is several orders of magnitude higher than the amount of tritium produced by an equivalent amount of fission energy. In a thermonuclear power economy, tritium management could be a much more significant problem."

6

It happens that George Woodwell at Brookhaven National Laboratory has studied the effects of radiation upon a forest on Long Island, one of the very few sustained experiments to determine the impact of pollution upon an ecosystem. Dr. Woodwell believes it is broadly instructive of the effect of pollution generally upon natural systems.

A late successional pine-oak forest was subjected to chronic irradiation from cesium-137, and the picture that emerges is that of nature beating an orderly retreat under increasing environmental severity. Five concentric zones surround the cesium source. Farthest out, where the radiation intensity is minimal, there is no obvious alteration in the composition of the forest although small changes in rates of growth could be measured. In zone four, the second outermost ring, the pines were eliminated. Moving to the midway ring three, all trees are gone; it is a shrub area. Zone two supports only sedges and grasses. No higher plants survive in the central ravaged zone closest to the cesium, only certain mosses and lichens.

What happens is succession as we discussed it earlier, only in reverse! A retrogression. A movement from complexity to simplification, as in moving from tropical rain forest to deciduous-conifer forest to grassland to tundra. There are other parallels. Dr. Woodwell says that "radiation and repeated fires both reduce the structure of the forest in similar ways, favoring low-growing hardy species." The early victims from the smog of Los Angeles are the conifer trees on 161,000 acres of national forests in Southern California.

A study of the oxides of sulfur emitted from smelters in Sudbury, Ontario, reveals rings of graduated devastation similar to those at the Brookhaven forest. "This example confirms the pattern of change," says Dr. Woodwell, "first a reduction of diversity of the forest by elimination of sensitive species; then elimination of the tree canopy and survival of resistant shrubs and herbs widely recognized as . . . successional species or 'generalists.' "

The pattern is the same for the five million acres in Vietnam that have been sprayed with herbicides. With the breakdown of the vegetation, the nutrient minerals leak out of the ecosystem into streams and rivers, causing eutrophication. With the depletion of nutrients, the forests are unable to rebuild to their former complexity. "It is no surprise," ecologist Woodwell writes, "that the extremely diverse forest canopies of Viet Nam when sprayed repeatedly with herbicides are replaced over large areas by dense stands of species of bamboo." What we know as jungles actually are the tangled second growths in areas where the virgin tropical rain forest was disturbed by man.

Dr. Woodwell writes in "Effects of Pollution on the Structure and Physiology of Ecosystems":

"The problems caused by pollution are of interest from two viewpoints. Practical people—toxicologists, engineers, health physicists, public health officials, intensive users of environment—consider pollution primarily as a direct hazard to man. Others, no less concerned for human welfare but with less pressing public responsibilities, recognize that toxicity to humans is but one aspect of the pollution problem, the other being a threat to the maintenance of a biosphere suitable for life as we know it."

Dr. Woodwell notes that successional patterns are a product of the evolution of life, that biological evolution has built the earth's ecosystems, and that these systems have been the dominant influence of earth throughout the span of human existence. He goes on:

"The structure of these systems is now being changed all over the world. We know enough about the structure and function of these systems to predict the broad outline of the effects of pollution on both land and water. We know that as far as our interests in the next decades are concerned, pollution operates on the time scale of succession, not of evolution, and we cannot look to evolution to cure this set of problems. The loss of structure involves a shift away from complex arrangements of specialized species toward the generalists; away from forest, toward hardy shrubs and herbs; away from those phytoplankton of the open ocean that (Charles) Wurster proved so very sensitive to DDT, toward those algae of the sewage plants that are unaffected by almost everything including DDT and most fish; away from diversity in birds, plants, and fish toward monotony; away from tight nutrient cycles toward very loose ones with terrestrial systems becoming depleted, and with aquatic systems becoming overloaded; away from stability toward instability especially with regard to sizes of populations of small rapidly reproducing organisms such as insects and rodents that compete with man; away from a world that runs itself through a self-augmentative, slowly moving evolution, to one that requires constant tinkering to patch it up, a tinkering that is malignant in that each act of repair generates a need for further repairs to avert problems generated at compound interest.

"This is the pattern, predictable in broad outline, aggravated by almost any pollutant. Once we recognize the pattern, we can begin to see the meaning of some of the changes occurring now in the earth's biota. We can see the demise of carnivorous birds and predict the demise of important fisheries. We can tell why, around industrial cities, hills that were once forested, now are not; why each single species is important; and how the increase in the temperature of natural water bodies used to cool new reactors will, by augmenting respiration over photosynthesis, ultimately degrade the system and contribute to degradation of other interconnected ecosystems nearby. We can begin to speculate on where continued exponential progress in this direction will lead: probably not to extinction—man will be around for a long time yet—but to a general degradation of the quality of life.

"The solution? Fewer people, unpopular but increasing restrictions on technology (making it more and more expensive), and a concerted effort to tighten up human ecosystems to reduce their interactions with the rest of the earth on whose stability we all depend. This does not require foregoing nuclear energy; it requires that if we must dump heat, it should be dumped into civilization to enhance a respiration rate in a sewage plant or an agricultural ecosystem, not dumped outside of civilization to affect that fraction of the earth's biota that sustains the earth as we know it. The question of what fraction that might be remains as one of the great issues, still scarcely considered by the scientific community."

CHAPTER NINE

The Ruptured Chain

1

MR. OR MRS. AVERAGE AMERICAN generates one-quarter of a pound of feces a day. That's a national daily production of more than 50 million pounds or 23,000 long tons of waste matter, as it's called in polite and sanitation circles. Since this material is esthetically repulsive to humans, has ceased to be nourishing to humans, and is medically harmful to humans, it is regarded *ergo* as waste. Also, since it is impossible to turn off this production, the problem becomes how to get rid of the stuff.

Civilized men have found various solutions to the problem. Medieval privies built into the depths of stone castles, such as the Tower of London, discharged through apertures to allow the contents to dribble down the face of the wall into the moat below. But the solution favored today is the water closet or flush toilet, the innovation of a Victorian gentleman named Thomas Crapper who gave his name to the language as a common noun.

Men were quick to connect the water closet to the built-in removal facility of the nearby waterway. In New York City, this was accomplished when private citizens surreptitiously linked their water closets to the municipal storm sewers until finally the bastard system was legitimatized.

At one time, Americans were world-famous for the efficacy of their plumbing, but this reputation has become tarnished because of the neglect of what happened to the material once it passed through the gleaming bathroom fixtures. A survey by *The New York Times* at the beginning of summer, 1970, found raw sewage as well as other pollutants in tidal bays in Florida, Georgia, South Carolina, Virginia, Maryland, Delaware, New Jersey, New York, Massachusetts, Maine, Alabama, Mississippi, Louisiana, Texas, and California.

It has been estimated that each American contributes 135 gallons of sewage (contaminated water) a day. This organic material requires or unites with dissolved oxygen (DO) in the water; the total oxygen requirement for any effluent is known as biochemical oxygen demand (BOD). The dumping of sewage uses up DO, making the water unsuitable for fish and other animals, although the water in a river can become reoxygenated as it moves along. Turbulent ocean water completely saturated with DO carries 10 ppm of oxygen, but 5 ppm is sufficient to support most aquatic life. In order to maintain that 5-ppm level, 4,000 gallons of water are needed to purify or dilute each individual's 135 gallons of daily sewage. At this rate, the entire flow of the United States would self-purify the sewage of no more than about 250 million people if they were perfectly distributed.

At present, about half that number of Americans—120 million—are served by sewers. But since industrial wastes have a BOD three times as great, it becomes immediately clear why virtually all 22 major river basins in the United States are degraded or endangered. Twenty percent of the sewer systems (1962 figures) dump raw sewage; 30 percent provide primary treatment—removal of solids and about one-third of the BOD—and 50 percent secondary treatment

—removal of up to 90 percent of the BOD. But, still, about one-half of the nitrogen and one-third of the phosphorous remain in the residual sludge, and these nutrients contribute substantially to the eutrophication of American waters.

Since the nitrates and other nutrients in human sewage provide nourishment for bacteria, algae, plant life, and other organisms in the waterways, it becomes apparent that human "wastes" are nothing of the sort. They are simply another resource out of place. Here we have farmers buying artificially produced nitrates to encourage growth of crops at the same time naturally produced—inevitably produced —nitrates from humans and farm animals go into waters to stimulate unwanted biological growth.

If Americans don't drown in eutrophic waters, then a "solid waste" burial awaits them. The results of productive prodigality are impressive. Every year we produce 48 billion more cans, 28 billion more bottles and jars, 10 million more cars and trucks, half a billion pounds more of plastic. At the same time, the Southern California desert is becoming a 16 million acre garbage dump, roadways are littered with beer cans, seven million autos are junked each year (more than 1,100 a week are abandoned on New York City streets), and plastic sheets float on the ocean's surface until sufficient algae accumulates to cause them to sink and continue their immortal existence on the ocean's floor. Each American creates about 10 pounds of refuse each day; half of it is carted away. The doubling rate for garbage is 17 years. The solid waste problem, like evil genies that have escaped from thousands of bottles, looms over almost every major American city. Nowhere is the problem more pressing than in New York City where the city's "Environmental Prospects—1970" discusses the subject under the title, "The Solid Waste Crisis." In 1975, the city's last great landfill at Fresh Kills, Staten Island, is expected to be shut down, leaving a gap of perhaps eight or more thousand tons of garbage a day that must be disposed of somehow. Several super-incinerators are being planned and other technologies studied.

But New York City already is displaying an inability to keep the city clean as the cost of sanitation grows every year. The problem, says Russell Cummings, the regional director of the Federal Bureau of Solid Waste Management, is that more people are throwing away more things and if the problem can be solved in New York City, it can be solved anywhere.

The problem is, first, that solid wastes are looked upon as "wastes"; second, that the "problem" is assigned to a miniscule segment of our society; and third, that no government takes a holistic view of the process. All of these conditions reflect ignorance of ecology. Economics is so divorced from ecological principles that it and all its practitioners, political adherents, administrators, and champions have sailed through the looking glass and no longer can see reality. Or they may simply be too busy manipulating dials on the cornucopia. But reality will not be ignored indefinitely, and the "solid waste problem" will force the most recalcitrant to become ecological converts.

2

Former New York City Sanitation Commissioner Samuel Kearing, Jr., says, "Today, more than 50 per cent of municipal refuse consists of paper, but a practical process for separating paper from run-of-the-mill refuse does not exist. Of course, if the cost of disposal were applied to the cost of the product—it costs six to eight dollars a ton just to burn paper in a New York incinerator—the entire picture would change. Suddenly the manufacturers of newsprint and cardboard containers could justify investments to reclaim and recycle used paper."

Once more we meet the problem of "external costs." An economic policy that does not reflect true costs—one that is inconsistent with reality—produces distortions. Oil and other mineral depletion allowances are examples. These incentives were deliberately instituted by Federal policy in order to encourage exploitation of natural resources a century ago. But today's need is no longer exploitation, but conservation of resources, reduction of pollution, recycling of wastes. All these ends would be served by removal of all depletion allowances and instituting tax incentives to recycle.

With such incentives no one can doubt how quickly used locomotive engine oil would be conserved and repurified and resold instead of finding its way into the Hudson River and other American waterways. No one can doubt that technology would respond to policy, as it naturally does, for technology's proper role is servant, not master. The reason technology overwhelms us is that today's policy is *laissez faire*, that is, no policy. This has nothing to do with capitalism or socialism, but everything to do with ecology. It has everything to do with ultimate consumption of resources, degradation of environment, and quality of life—or, to put it another way, impoverishment of the nation.

Composting is a system of taking organic garbage, shredding it, and converting it to topsoil, a resource that is being washed away in the United States. However, composting is a marginal or virtually non-existent operation because, despite its ecological validity and fundamental value to the country, it cannot be made to pay. Another case of economics at war with ecology.

"As Sanitation Commissioner," says Kearing, "I was unable to find a single paper manufacturer interested in discussing the recycling of paper. I was told it was cheaper to grow pulpwood than to reclaim used material."

As it happened, the Garden State Paper Company of Garfield, New Jersey, already was in business converting used paper into competitive newsprint. In 1969, the company—with plants now in Pomona, California, and Alsip, Illinois, as well as Garfield—converted 365,000 tons of old newspapers into 320,000 tons of fresh newsprint. The firm sold the newsprint for 12 dollars less a ton than paper made from virgin pulp and total business for its paper output was 45 million dollars. The reused newsprint production amounts to 11 percent of total U.S. manufacture and 4 percent of U.S. consumption. A spokesman for the American Forest Institute said that newsprint made from reclaimed newspaper conserved more than five million trees —not to mention the conservation in the solid waste problem. Moreover the reused newsprint can be reprocessed again and again with a 10 to 15 percent loss in material.

Professor C. H. Waddington of the Institute of Animal Genetics in Edinburgh told an international Symposium of Man-Made Changes in the Environment in London in September, 1969, "It has been calculated that to provide every adult of the world population (of the year 2000—an estimated seven billion) with a small two sheet newspaper and three sheets of toilet paper a day would require a fourfold increase in the area of forests if the paper continued to be manufactured from wood."

In addition to paper, Americans discard each year 10 million tons of iron and steel worth nearly 200 million dollars. Almost one million tons of aluminum, copper, lead, zinc, tin, and other nonferrous metals are thrown away; also 15 million tons of glass and other worthwhile, recoverable materials. In all, the energy value of United States "waste" annually is equivalent to 60 million tons of coal (Paris burns garbage to produce some of its electricity). The total scrap and energy value of the wastes is close to one billion dollars.

The principal problem in metal recovery, as in paper, is separation of the items. "A tremendous potential in recycling and recovery lies in the seven million automobiles junked every year," says S. Fred Singer, Deputy Assistant Secretary for Scientific Programs in the Interior Department. "A major problem is to eliminate copper which is a troublesome impurity. The eventual answer may lie in educating our manufacturers, and indeed all manufacturers, to pay great attention to the ultimate fate of the article they manufacture and to design it so that it can be easily recycled. Various positive and negative tax incentives could be used to accelerate the educational process."

"The appropriate role for the federal government," says former New York City Sanitation Commissioner Kearing, "is to institute regulations to limit the production of solid waste, liquid waste and air-polluting emissions." Permitting these wastes, he says, "constitutes an enormous subsidy to industry and the consumer economy at the expense of the environment. It encourages, indeed makes inevitable, the practice of built-in obsolescence and disposability . . ."

By working on a water pollution study for the Ecological Society of America, limnologist Gerald Lauer was led to the inevitable conclusion that "waste" simply represents a rupture of the recycling system. Even in a natural ecosystem, Dr. Lauer points out, if too many deer congregate, their droppings can pollute a lake. In urban concentrations, the foods and products come from outlying areas, are used, what is left is dumped into water, air, or land. Nothing is recycled back to the land whence it came. The nutrients from the soil of Kansas are dumped as raw sewage into the

Hudson River or as sewage sludge into the Atlantic Ocean. The iron from Minnesota rusts on auto skeletons in junk yards in the Bronx and New Jersey. "When resources are depleted, men will mine trash heaps and be glad to do it. But why must we wait until the resources are gone?" In order to recycle, Dr. Lauer says, we must think in terms of spending as much money and energy in getting so-called waste products back to areas of origin as we do in getting new products to users.

Geophysicist Athelstan Spilhaus, 1970 president of the American Association for the Advancement of Science, says that the first industrial revolution was hailed as a way of ennobling human beings by substituting steam and electrical power for their muscles. But along with that came air pollution, which was degrading to human existence. The second revolution, Dr. Spilhaus says, brought about the multiplication of "things," mass-produced things so that people could have more and more. But this also generated the solid waste problem. A third industrial revolution, he says, gave us tremendous growth in industrial chemicals for all purposes. But many of them—pesticides, for example— turned out to be not selective, and they damaged natural systems and polluted the environment.

"I believe we must base the next industrial revolution—a planned one—on the thesis that there is no such thing as waste, that waste is simply some useful substance that we do not yet have the wit to use. In the next industrial revolution, there must be a loop back from the user to the factory, which industry must close." Dr. Spilhaus notes that, in general, the private sector makes things before use while the public sector disposes of them after use. If private industry does not enter into the rest of the cycle, he believes, then recycling will be much more difficult because products will not be designed for reuse. Also, with industry operating ever more efficiently and more workers going into services, the public sector will become bloated and unwieldy.

It is clear that the problem of "wastes" is bound up with pollution, overburdening natural ecosystems, externalities and the economic distortions of ecological reality, recycling, the impossibility of an open system of materials; the interrelatedness of all, and the interdependence of all upon environment in a closed system: in short, the principles of ecology.

An awareness and movement are beginning. The Reynolds Aluminum Company has begun a scrap program. Three months after criticism of no-return bottles by the President's Special Assistant for Consumer Affairs, the Glass Container Manufacturers Institute announced a nation-wide program to buy used bottles, at a penny a pound, for reuse in the making of new bottles. The Institute hoped to recover about 40 percent of the bottles made each year. National legislation was passed in the fall of 1970 to encourage methods to recover resources from waste and other legislation has been proposed to require an industry fee on packaging materials not easily disposed. Such a fee not only would discourage excessive packaging and therefore reduce solid wastes, but the money would revert to cities to help pay for clean-up.

General Motors has developed a method for reclaiming metal scrap left when fenders, hoods, and other body parts are stamped out. A multidisciplinary group at Clemson University has been working on a disposable bottle. Another team, headed by a University of Toronto chemist, announced the perfection of a plastic that would disintegrate when exposed to sunlight, but remain intact indoors.

Ingenuity and invention await only coherent leadership. Technology, the servant, is waiting for its masters to learn that the laws of ecology can be neither ignored nor defied indefinitely, that waste, like pollution, is a measure of the ignorance and defiance.

It will be interesting to see how much filth, how high the mountains of trash must accumulate, before the masters obey.

CHAPTER TEN

By Their Fruits You Shall Know Them

1

"THROUGH THE CAR WINDOW I can see the fences which line a road about 100 feet from the track. Beyond that is blackness, impenetrable and forbidding, through which we have been traveling for nearly 200 miles.

"I have not seen more than two automobiles on the road that parallels the railroad track for a hundred miles or more. I have seen human beings only when passing bleak villages, consisting of a few shacks. Houses empty, yards empty. I have not seen a single child in these ghostlike, pathetic villages. Trees, once in a while. But their naked branches are gray with dust. They look like ghosts of trees, shackled and strangled by this choking thing . . .

"A passenger told me, 'on one trip through here, in a distance of a few hundred feet I counted 40 jack rabbits stretched out, choked to death by dust. You don't see any wildlife out here, 'cept maybe a few crows. No songbirds, and hardly any cattle. Yet right in this spot we're passing through, the cattle herds used to be as thick as flies.' There was a mystified look on his face. It is an expression I have seen on the faces of others on the train. They can't understand this outburst of nature, this dissipation of the soil

217

which has fed us. I saw fear in their faces, as of impending disaster."

That was the Dust Bowl as George Greenfield described it in *The New York Times* on March 8, 1937. That was what happened when cattle ranchers and sheep herders allowed their stock to overgraze the grasslands, when men tilled and planted wheat and cotton in topsoil too thin for an anchoring medium, and when these practices were compounded by drought. At the time, the U.S. Soil Conservation Service estimated 50 million acres—nine million of them on the Great Plains—ruined by erosion; another 175 million acres seriously eroded or wasted of most topsoil. That was more than 10 percent of the land area of the United States at that time.

The Dust Bowl was the most massive overt warning in the lives of contemporary people that men may not do anything they wish to the land with impunity. Agriculture took the lesson to heart. Soil conservation became a respectable term and farmers came to understand that certain lands could not be cultivated and others only with careful techniques such as contour plowing. In the 1940s, the drought ended, and not very long after that agriculture was transfigured by the Industrial-Technological Revolution. The Dust Bowl faded from memories like the buried civilizations of the past.

Until agriculture was revolutionized in the United States after the Second World War, it had been conducted in principally the same fashion as the practice that emancipated the human species from hunting and grubbing for existence some seven to ten thousand years ago. With that agriculture the species had grown from a few million individuals to more than two billion.

Agriculture is a simplified ecosystem and therefore a relatively unstable one. It is an early successional community, so that without the constant intervention of the farmer, it would yield to other plant forms and revert to whatever biome it belonged. The crops consist of introduced plant species which are well adapted to grow on disturbed sites. Not only is the ecosystem simplified, but the farmer aims to confine it to the predetermined plant species, so that the nutrients of the soil go into the one cultigen to be harvested. Furthermore, he tries to help each plant produce as much surplus—capture and fix as much energy—as possible. In a mature forest ecosystem, all the energy is going to maintenance of the stable biomass and in leakage—the energy which is siphoned off by insects and other members of the animal community—so that there is no annual surplus to harvest. In the managed agricultural ecosystem, the farmer tries to eliminate all energy leakage with insecticides, fungicides, herbicides, and rodenticides.

If the agricultural revolution partially freed men from the natural system, then the industrial-technological revolution has almost freed men from agriculture. In the United States, five percent of the population produces the food and fiber for the entire nation with surpluses to export for an additional 100 million people. In India, 95 percent of the population is involved in agriculture.

In 1800, when the effective instrument was the sickle, it took 56 hours of labor to produce one acre of wheat. By 1880, when the horse-drawn reaper was in use, it took 20 man-hours to grow and harvest an acre of wheat. In the 1960s, it took less than two hours to do the job better. There were nearly 27 million horses and mules on American farms in 1917; their number dropped to three million by 1960. During that same time the number of tractors increased from about 50,000 to some five million. One mechanical cotton picker is equivalent to 80 human cotton picking hands. The modern farm technology has made many a farm product a good year-round buy. Even the most desultory visitor to the supermarket can appreciate the variety available to satisfy his hunger or whim. The supermarket is the American realization of the ancient Greek dream of the cornucopia.

American agriculture is so productive that the U.S. Department of Agriculture paid farmers three and a half billion dollars in 1969 and again in 1970 for *not* growing something. Judged on the basis of quality and quantity of products and on their availability—manifested in the size of American children and the girth of their parents—on the efficiency of the production, and on the liberation of a population from obtaining food, the achievement of American agriculture surely ranks with the significant achievements in all human history.

But, as ecology teaches, human endeavors cannot be evaluated by arbitrarily restricted standards. *All* effects must be entered into the ledger for an accurate accounting.

Perhaps the most obvious and paradoxical effect is that this farming has not been good for most farmers. While production efficiency nearly doubled that in other industries, the number of farmers dwindled. Twenty million Americans lived on farms in 1950; 10 million today. While farm values increased, the number of farms went down. In 1935, there were 6.8 million farms, in 1961 about 3.7 million, today about three million. And of these farms, one million produced most of the 50 billion dollars a year in crops and earned most of the 16 billion dollars in net farm income in 1969.

Looked at one way, the reduction of farm workers can be regarded as an improvement in efficiency. Looked at another, it is a growing national weakness—an inability to provide jobs, a self-liquidating reservoir of farm talent.

While the rural poor are a burden on the nation, the

migration of eliminated farm workers and their families to urban areas fueled and exacerbated the nation's major domestic problem of the 1960s—the breakdown of cities. While a rural problem was deftly shifted to urban areas, the Federal Government in 1969 still spent more for farmers and on farm subsidies than it did for hunger, housing, urban transportation, or water pollution—all problems resulting from or allied to agricultural "achievements."

Even within the farm community, most of that money went to those top million producers while the rest just held on or foundered. Edward Higbee, a professor of land utilization at the University of Rhode Island, wrote in *Farms and Farmers in an Urban Age*, "If he is not naive, the urbanite should know by now that the nation's agricultural economy is not designed to help just anyone who calls himself a farmer. Rather, it is designed to bolster the agricultural economy so as to make farming profitable for those able to invest fresh capital in it." In other words, the primary goal of today's agricultural industrialist is not to produce food, but to produce money.

Along with greatly increased production and efficiency have come the other concomitants of early industrial revolution: factory conditions for poultry and livestock, cutthroat competition, utter disregard for environment, and subjugation of considerations for the future to immediate profits. In a replaying of Garrett Hardin's tragedy of the commons in which law-abiding citizens through self-interest exhaust a resource, big farmers are rushing to tap for irrigation a vast groundwater reservoir, the Ogallala pool, which has been accumulating for centuries under parts of Texas, Oklahoma, Colorado, Kansas, and Nebraska.

The industrial-agricultural system pursues one method in order to achieve its production wonders. It maximizes monoculture—one-crop farming—so that complex machinery can be used with greatest effect. It also enhances yield through experimenting with genetic strains; fans production through irrigation and intensive use of chemical fertilizers; and it protects the yield with chemical pesticides.

Ecologists regard most of these practices with foreboding. Says Robert Rudd of the University of California at Davis: "We have had seven thousand years of agriculture in which, through empirical methods and decisions, we have acquired an essentially stable and useful producing agroecosystem. What has happened in the last two or three decades? We have discarded much of the tested procedures and are now exposing the whole system to new procedure and chemicals."

"Most Americans think our agriculture is wonderful," says William Cooper of Michigan State University. "But in the long term, considering its imbalance with the environment, it is not."

Thirty-five years ago, horses were used on farms, not machines powered by fossil fuel. The fuel was oats and hay, produced on the farm, with all wastes returned to the farm. When the change was made from horses to machines, the efficiency improved in terms of dollars but not in terms of energy invested. We have seen a growing infusion of energy from fossil fuel—to cultivate and harvest crops, to manufacture and transport pesticides and fertilizers, to provide and control irrigation—so that the gain in modern industrial agricultural production is more apparent than real. This discrepancy will be erased with the exhaustion of crude oil unless some energy substitute can be found.

Ecologically, farming went from a balanced to an unbalanced system. American farmers consider the ancient rice-paddy agriculture of Southeast Asia inefficient and not particularly productive. But, Dr. Cooper says, in such a closed system, the minerals are not permanently exported off the soil. Animal and human wastes are added back into the system. Most of what is removed is the carbon dioxide, the water, and the energy portion of the food crop, all of which are readily replenished from the atmosphere and sun.

"The paddy rice system is one of the world's most elegant ecological systems," says John Cantlon also of M.S.U. And he fears what will happen to this stable agricultural system with the introduction of American methods, an eventuality that has already begun. It is known as the Green Revolution. Western agriculture has developed new genetic strains of rice, wheat, and corn that can produce at much higher rates than the old Asian and Latin American varieties. Implantation of these new strains already has begun in India, the Philippines, Malaysia, Indonesia, and Pakistan.

"When we send them a new rice variety with capacity for high production," Dr. Cantlon says, "we send plants with lower genetic background and less resistance to pests. These new varieties need, besides fertilizers to help them produce, pesticides.

"We fail to understand the complete ecological system. We forget that these people also intensively fish the canals that regulate water in the rice paddies. If the pesticides kill those sensitive fresh water shrimp and other animal foods that the people depend upon for their meager supply of protein, will the nutritional status of the people be as sound as it now is? Might not the highly toxic organic phosphates poison the people themselves as they work waist deep in the water of the rice fields and canals?"

Already there are indications that the big landowners with capital to invest in the technology stand to benefit most. Already it is apparent that it would be advantageous to break up the old small family farms for the more efficient big farms. Wrote the *London Economist*'s correspondent: "The new rice technology has added to the displacement of farm laborers. The widespread use of one-man machines produced in Japan is driving unemployed peasants to the slum fringes of the cities. It must be noted that the rice revolution could contain the seeds of a revolution of another kind."

Newsweek in August, 1970, reported that "ironically, it is India's widely heralded 'green revolution' . . . that now seems to be forcing many sharecroppers and subsistence farmers to the wall." The article listed the thousands of eviction suits pending and reported that Communists were capitalizing on the unrest. What is needed, the article said, is land reform, but that is coming very slowly. "Meanwhile, a situation is brewing that could eventually turn India's green revolution an angry shade of red."

It is one thing to say that efficient, super-productive agriculture is "freeing labor for other occupations," as it is euphemistically phrased in the United States—but it should be obvious how much more socially destructive such a course is in non-industrialized and labor-glutted countries of Asia.

2

California is the most important agricultural state in the United States. It produces 43 percent of the nation's fresh vegetables, 42 percent of its fruits. The heart of that agriculture is the San Joaquin Valley, 300 miles long, 50 miles wide: eight million of the most fertile acres in the country. The valley is bisected by the San Joaquin River which flows south to north and empties into the eastern part of San Francisco Bay. The river is a trough through the center of the valley. More than a century ago, farmers began diverting waters from feeder streams to irrigate their croplands.

Supply from this source was undependable, particularly during summer months, and farmers resorted to pumping groundwater. But this method was expensive. About a century ago, the first construction began of diversion dams and canals to conduct water considerable distances from major streams.

By about 1930, the valley had reached its irrigation capacity based on the natural system of streams and wells. More than two million acres were under irrigation. In the 1940s, man began a major transformation of the hydrology of the valley with the building of Shasta Dam on the Sacramento River to the north and Friant Dam on the San Joaquin River. So much water was diverted from the San Joanquin River for irrigation that the Delta Mendota Canal was constructed along the west side of the San Joaquin Valley to bring water from the Sacramento River, before it emptied into San Francisco Bay, south to replace depleted San Joanquin River waters. At this point, the San Joaquin no longer was a natural river, but became largely a drain to carry off agricultural waste waters.

Irrigation aims to keep soil around roots continuously moist and continuously supplied with nutrients. An unwanted effect is that the water evaporates, leaving behind its dissolved salts. To circumvent the buildup of mineral salts in the soil, extra water is applied so that water and salts percolate downward out of the root zone. But this is a perilous policy, because of the danger that salts will leach out of the soil into the groundwater whence there is no exit. In order to avoid this, the percolating water is intercepted by a shallow drainage system which conducts the brackish water into drainage wells.

Even so, Frank Stead, onetime Chief of California's Division of Environmental Sanitation, writes, "It is estimated that 400 million tons of salt have built up in the soils of the valley floor, and the groundwater itself in some areas has a high enough content of dissolved salts to be toxic to plants."

This seems to be the appropriate place to recall the skeletal irrigation canals buried with lost civilizations in the sands between the Tigris and Euphrates rivers.

The State of California and Bureau of Reclamation hope to relieve drainage problems with a master drain to be built the length of the valley on its west side. This is necessary also because of expanded irrigation under the state's three billion dollar California Water Plan, a complicated arrangement of shifting water from the north to the south that has embroiled citizens in tangled controversy. The plan would divert still more water from the Sacramento River, raising fears that already degraded San Francisco Bay no longer would be properly flushed. More water in the Los Angeles area will mean more development, more people, more cars —when what is needed is more clean air.

What is taking place in California appears to be a grandiose, rococo illustration of ecologist George Woodwell's observation: ". . . away from a world that runs itself . . . to one that requires constant tinkering to patch it up, a tinkering that is malignant in that each act of repair generates a need for further repairs to avert problems generated at compound interest."

Cultivation in Egypt along the Nile River began about the same time as agriculture in Mesopotamia, but, unlike the practice in the Asian area, has survived and supported the world's longest continuous civilization. The agriculture was restricted to a narrow belt on either side of the great river and was based on the annual surge and ebb of floodwaters.

In an effort to expand Egypt's arable land and increase production to support a larger population, the nation built the Aswan Dam, which in addition to storing irrigation waters in Lake Nasser also would generate electric power and provide flood control. The dam went into operation in 1964, and the new irrigation system did open new croplands.

But the dam also stopped the annual flow of silt down the river, silt freighted with nutrients that perennially enriched the valley soil. A measure of the resulting impoverishment is given by the Egyptian sardine catch in the Mediterranean: 18,000 tons in 1965, down to 500 tons in 1968. The infusion of silt also replenished soil washed away in the delta; now erosion along the lower Nile threatens to remove as much productive farmland as that gained from irrigation.

Further, there is concern that the groundwater level may be raised to such a degree by the water impounded behind the dam or by seepage from the irrigation canals that dissolved mineral salts will be raised sufficiently high to salinize the productive soil layer. Such toxicity has materialized in an older British irrigation project in Pakistan.

As if such unwanted effects were not enough, the new irrigation system provides a favorable environment for snails that are the vector for a debilitating and virtually incurable parasitic disease, schistosomiasis. While residents of the delta areas always have been exposed to this life-shortening illness, the snail now flourishes in the slow-moving waters of the constantly filled irrigation ditches.

In 1970, scientists at the American University in Beirut, Lebanon, detected in the eastern Mediterranean Sea still another undesirable effect of the new agriculture—16 to 20 parts of the persistent pesticide heptachlor per million parts of fish. "This is so high," said assistant biology professor John Burchard, "that if a man ate 400 grams of such fish each day he'd be sick or dead in two years."

3

Agricultural wastes, the Interior Department's S. Fred Singer told the 136th American Association for the Advancement of Science Meeting in December, 1969, "constitute the largest solid waste problem in the United States." Two billion tons of sediment wash from farmlands into the nation's rivers and streams each year. Zeroing in on pollution, Dr. Singer said, "The chief problems come from the improper application of and excess application of fertilizers, from pesticides which wash into rivers or vaporize into the atmosphere, and from organic wastes, particularly from feedlots, which are allowed to wash into rivers; 10,000 cattle produce as much waste as a city of 165,000." Animal wastes in the United States are equivalent to the wastes of one billion people.

This is one tine of the three-pronged pollution problem resulting from the new agriculture. Industrial farming has one overriding criterion—productivity, return on the dollar —and industrial farmers discovered that cattle and other farm animals grow faster if confined. Hence the animals are immured in feedlots with a consequent buildup of enormous amounts of manure. Dr. Singer said that one technological fix may be compulsory waste treatment plants for these overcrowded centers.

In the fall of 1969, Great Britain adopted a set of codes to govern intensive or factory farming, the first nation to do so. In explaining the new liberalized rules, Secretary of State for Scotland William Ross said calves would have enough room to move sideways, to be able to groom themselves, and to lie down.

A member of the House of Commons asked, "What about turning around?"

Mr. Ross turned and was understood to reply, "It may not be in the best interests of the animal to turn around."

The confining of animals means not only that their wastes pollute waterways, but that the nutritive manure no longer is distributed over the land to fertilize crops. To plug the rift in that ancient recycling system, U.S. farmers bought and applied seven million tons of chemical nitrogen in 1969.

Not only has manure been converted from desirable fertilizer to a burdensome pollutant, but Barry Commoner wonders what the practice of substituting an unnatural nitrogen fertilizer for the natural one is doing to the farmers' and nation's most indispensible commodity—the soil. Dr. Commoner, professor of plant physiology and director of the Center for the Biology of Natural Systems at Washington University, refers to the Sanborn Field studies "a typical and classical study of that heroic period in agricultural research." The studies began at the Agricultural Experiment Station in Missouri in 1888 and continued for half a century. The experimenters observed fields cultivated with proper crop rotation and (a) left unfertilized, (b) fertilized with manure, and (c) fertilized with chemical nitrate.

The unfertilized fields deteriorated; they lost organic nitrogen and for most crops their soil produced about one-half the yield of the plots treated with manure. The production of the fields treated with natural fertilizer increased production over the 50 years. The plots fertilized with chemical nitrate also produced good yields. Economically, the nitrate was as effective as the manure. But the soil treated with chemical fertilizer, like unfertilized soil, lost two-thirds of its original organic nitrogen. The 1942 report said:

"The organic matter content and the physical condition of the soil on the chemically treated plots have declined rapidly. These altered conditions have prevented sufficient water from percolating into the soil and being stored for drought periods. Apparently a condition has developed in the soil whereby the nutrients applied are not delivered to the plant when needed for optimum growth . . . Evidently most of the nitrogen not used by the immediate crop is removed from the soil by leaching or denitrification . . . From these figures it is evident that heavy application of chemical fertilizers have given a very low efficiency of recovery."

"The story is clear," wrote Dr. Commoner. "While nitrate fertilizer provided good support for the growth of the crop, it failed to rebuild the lost humic nitrogen. As a result, soil porosity deteriorated, aeration became more difficult and the plant roots, which must have oxygen if they are to absorb nutrients, were unable to take up all of the nitrate made available to them by the added fertilizer. The rest of the nitrate was lost from the soil. Some of it leached out in the soil water and runoff."

Nitrate from chemical fertilizers, from sewage and animal wastes, and phosphates from detergents are the prime agents for eutrophication of America's waters.

When the Sanborn Field report was published in 1942, less than 500,000 tons of chemical nitrogen were produced and used annually. By 1969, use of the chemical fertilizer increased 15 times—good news indeed for the agricultural chemical industry. But that billion-dollar industry had something else to stand up and cheer about during the post-war years.

4

Not only is the new agriculture a simplified ecosystem, but in order to make the most efficient use of machinery and increase productivity, it is based on mass planting of one species. This monoculture system is ecologically precarious. It takes the intrusion of but one limiting factor to ruin the entire ecosystem. Hence the artificial defenses: irrigation to supply the moisture, chemical fertilizers to guarantee the nutrients.

There is one other great hazard entailed in the concentration of a single species: it provides an attractive environment for predators, parasites, and pathogens. This was one of the lessons the human species had to learn the hard way during thousands of years of civilization—the massing of people in cities and towns provided the necessary densities to enable the epidemic spread of plague, malaria, influenza, and other diseases. Nothing could be done about these attacks until humans adopted more sanitary methods and finally discovered the transmission mechanisms of disease.

Similarly, through the ages insects took their tithes of agricultural crops; fungi and disease pathogens survived at the expense of plants. From these symbioses, plant resistance evolved and while crop acreage remained at modest proportions there was never enough fodder assembled in one place for most insects to emulate the occasional locust plagues. With widespread single species cultivation during the past century, enough food was provided for plant-specific insects to make pests out of themselves. After the pests came pesticides.

But it was not until the chemical revolution during World War Two that agriculture suddenly gained a portfolio of poisons of unprecedented power. The accomplishments of DDT in World War Two back to back with the miracles of penicillin created a mood of acceptance and expectation. This is the way *Business Week* hailed DDT November 25, 1944, in a "Report to Executives: What's Coming in Chemicals":

"With such a product to stimulate additional research, mankind has new weapons promising eventual freedom from disease-bearing insects such as lice, fleas, flies, mosquitoes, and ticks; from household pests such as moths, cockroaches, and bedbugs, and from the insects that frequently kill crops, orchards, and shade trees."

Four years later, Paul Mueller, the employee of a Swiss chemical firm who first recognized the insecticidal qualities of DDT, was awarded a Nobel Prize for Medicine. In April, 1951, the *American Journal of Public Health* cited country after country where DDT had drastically reduced typhus and malaria and concluded its editorial with; "This is one of the most dramatic and significant chapters in the entire history of public health."

In this climate, it is perhaps not surprising that agriculture turned trustingly, almost religiously, to chemical control of pests with DDT and other chlorinated hydrocarbons in the van. These organochlorines, as they are also called, had two enormous virtues in the eyes of agriculture—first, they were persistent, they stayed around for a long time killing crop pests. This saved the farmer time, energy, and money in applications. In short, they were a good buy. Second, they were "broad spectrum" in that they were effective against a whole array of insects. This made them a particularly profitable product for manufacturers.

Everything went beautifully within the agricultural realm —pests were controlled and crop yields increased. But disquieting signs began to surface in other parts of the world. In 1962, Rachel Carson presented the data then available in *Silent Spring*.

That the indiscriminate broadcasting of powerful chemical poisons could do the human species in by contaminating its habitat was a concept that had not yet suggested itself and certainly was not entertained by any serious scientific study.

But spurred by the controversy scientists began to unravel the mysteries of the planet's most insidious pollution. It worked invisibly and could accomplish its decimation of fish and wildlife without even producing corpses! The persistence of DDT made it a candidate for the biogeochemical cycle. No one knew for sure how long it lasted, but studies indicated the chemical still possessed half its toxicity after 10 or 12 years. It was highly mobile—it could travel in water, in vapor, or become attached to dust particles and circulate through the atmosphere. It was soluble in fats, but not water. This meant it would not dilute in lakes and oceans, but gravitate to biological units and through biological systems. Not only through biological systems, but its concentration increased as it moved up a food chain. Obviously, each plankton would harbor a miniscule amount, but the crustacean that ate many plankton collected much more DDT. Fish predators of the crustaceans might concentrate ten times the amount of DDT as their prey. By this process of biological magnification, the carnivorous birds at the top of food chains ingested a burden of poison that interfered with reproduction.

This was still another deceptive station in the tortuous travels of the persistent pesticides: the sublethal effect. At a certain level, DDT will kill outright. But in chronic contamination of the environment, where the amounts of the poison are slowly building up in the fats of certain species, the organochlorine reaches a level short of killing, but blocking reproduction. This was found to be true in studies of trout and salmon. In the meantime, other investigators noted the disappearance and diminution of predator and scavenger birds—all at the tops of their food chains: ospreys, pelicans, grebes, peregrine falcons, Bermuda petrels, sparrow hawks and other hawks, and bald eagles. Researchers learned how this was accomplished in birds. The DDT caused a hormonal interference that depressed calcium production. With thin-shelled eggs, chicks had a less than normal chance to survive.

Scientists also began to realize from the appearance of many chemical pollutants that the oceans are the sumps of the world. A frightful picture began to emerge as the mists of ignorance cleared. Wherever one looked, there was DDT —in penguins in the Antarctic, in polar bears in the Arctic, in birds that lived far out in the Atlantic ocean, 19 parts per million in a random examination of a barracuda by the Food and Drug Administration. The persistent, mobile, fat-soluble poison also was building up through fresh water as well as marine communities. Kenneth Macek of the U.S. Fish-Pesticide Research Laboratory at Columbia, Missouri, said that 99 percent of samples taken from 50 fresh water stations during a two-year period showed concentrations of DDT. Dr. Macek said that the DDT level of most water in the United States was sufficient to cause reproductive failure among laboratory test fish. Crabs and oysters were particularly sensitive to the poison. Charles Wurster, a biochemist who spearheaded the fight against DDT with the Environmental Defense Fund, found that the chlorinated hydrocarbons reduce photosynthesis in four species of phytoplankton representing four major classes of algae—an omen of the gravest nature, since phytoplankton are major producers of oxygen.

Few people are legitimate global thinkers. Because of his professional work with ecosystems and biogeochemical cycles, George Woodwell qualifies as one of them. In March, 1969, Dr. Woodwell was asked what are our most serious pollution hazards. He replied: collection of pollutants in the atmosphere, thermal pollution, radiation, and contamination by pesticides. Pesticide contamination, he said, was foremost and the most immediate threat. With continued intensive use of persistent pesticides, Dr. Woodwell could foresee wholesale depletion of marine food fisheries because of reproductive failure. Such an eventuality would reduce agricultural gains to a trade-off, and an undesirable one at that.

Still, in this Kafkaesque nightmare, the U.S. Department of Agriculture was intransigent on limiting the use of persistent pesticides. They had not been proved directly harmful to humans. This refusal came despite one study that showed that a group of persons who had died from cancer carried double or more the amount of DDT residues in their fatty tissue than people who had been killed in accidents. The "normal" DDT burden for an American was about 10 ppm, three more ppm than the FDA permitted in the market sale of meat. This Federal attitude persisted despite the fact that human mother's milk was found to carry more DDT than the World Health Organization deemed safe, and despite the fact that Arizona had banned the pesticide because of high DDT levels in cows' milk.

Then, in the spring of 1969, the National Cancer Institute revealed a study which showed that DDT produced more than normal numbers of cancers in laboratory mice. This one report transformed the controversy. All of a sudden, DDT became a carcinogen. Under the Delaney Amendment to the Food and Drug Act, carcinogens must be banned from the marketplace. However, DDT is neither a food, a drug, nor a cosmetic. It just happened to be *in* food and *in* drinking water. So Agriculture was not bound and neither was HEW by FDA rules.

But pressure increased in 1969, when HEW seized 14 tons of coho salmon taken commercially from Lake Michigan because the fish had extremely high DDT levels—19 ppm. At that time, the FDA had not posted maximum permissable amounts for fish, but subsequently decided that five ppm was the proper tolerance level. The seizure of the salmon caused consternation not only in agriculture and the agricultural chemical industry, but also in the new Michigan sport fishing industry built upon catching, and eating, coho salmon. Now this was made pointless by contaminated fish. Michigan banned DDT for most uses.

After the most dogged, bitterly fought of all environmental encounters, the Agriculture Department in November, 1969, cancelled use of DDT on shade trees, tobacco plants, in marshes and estuaries, and in gardens and households. But U.S.D.A. persisted in guarding the bulk of the use of persistent pesticides.

The irony of this official recalcitrance is that the chemical pesticide technology already was bankrupt in the estimation of experts most familiar with the scene. It is not so difficult to understand why if one recalls that study by ecologists Hairston, Smith, and Slobodkin on limiting factors for different trophic levels. If light or space is the limiting factor for plants, and food is the limiting factor for carnivorous predators, the limiting factor for herbivores—insects —is *predators*. To rely solely on chemicals to eliminate insects not only was the wrong solution, but the technology actually favored the pests it was designed to control. This comes about because the broad spectrum pesticides kill the insects' predators as well as the insects. Since the insects have a larger population than their predators, they are more likely to have survivors. The insects breed faster, therefore they are more likely to develop resistant genotypes. And because of biological magnification, the predators carry a more lethal burden of the insecticide than the insect targets.

Recall *Business Week*'s euphoric forecast about the

chemical miracles to come and compare it with this assessment one human generation later by Robert van den Bosch, a professor of entomology, Division of Biological Control, University of California at Berkeley:

"If there is a group of animals that has met the competitive challenge of man and held its own, it is the Insecta. Abundance, diversity, and adaptability are the key characteristics that have helped insects to stand up to their more clever competitor. And quite ironically, man, the thinking animal, has actually played into his enemy's strength by relying overwhelmingly on a single combat technique—chemical control."

Dr. van den Bosch cites the fact that more than 200 pests (and these include the housefly, boll weevil, and many species of malarial mosquitoes) have become resistant to chemicals. He concludes: "As matters stand, we are at the brink of economic and ecological chaos in pest control. The insects are beating us in the competition game, and have forced us into an environmentally damaging strategy. We cannot continue our present course; it is a one-way street to ecological disaster."

Richard Doutt, Acting Dean of the College of Agricultural Sciences, and Ray Smith, Chairman of the Department of Entomology and Parasitology, both at Berkeley, gave the following analysis of cotton crop protection throughout the world:

Phase one is subsistence agriculture. There is no irrigation, rare or no insecticide treatments with growers relying on natural control, plant resistance, and luck. Yields are low and usually do not go on the world market. This is practiced today in Chad, Afghanistan, Uganda, and parts of Ecuador.

Phase two is what Drs. Doutt and Smith call the exploitation phase. Cotton frequently is one of the first crops chosen to exploit newly irrigated areas in developing countries. Crop protection schemes are introduced to protect the large crops as well as new plant varieties with good yields but poor insect resistance. "Unfortunately, in most cases, in the exploitation phase the crop protection schemes are dependent solely on chemical pesticides. They are used intensively and often on fixed schedules. At first these schemes are successful and desired yields of seed and lint are obtained."

This leads to the crisis phase. After a variable number of years in the profitable exploitation phase, growers notice that pests resurge quickly after pesticide treatment, even with more intensive applications, and finally the insecticide no longer has an effect upon the pests. "Another insecticide is substituted and the pest populations become tolerant to it, too, but this happens more rapidly than with the first chemicals. At the same time, pests that never cause damage in the area previously, or only occasionally, become serious and regular ravagers of the cotton fields. This combination of pesticide resistance, pest resurgence, and unleashed secondary pests causes greatly increased production costs."

Four, the disaster phase. "The pesticide usage increases production costs to the point where cotton can no longer be grown profitably. At first, marginal land and marginal farmers are removed from production. Eventually, cotton is no longer profitable to produce in the area. A number of Central American countries are now in this disaster phase. In the United States, this disaster phase has been postponed a bit by cotton subsidies."

What should come next, the authors say, is the integrated control phase, practiced today in several valleys in Peru. This is a broad-scale approach, using specialists from different disciplines, to modify the environment to keep insects from becoming pests. It does not equate pest control with total elimination. It believes that the most powerful control forces are natural ones and seeks to change environment to induce natural mortality in the pest population and to make fullest use of biological controls, that is, seeking out and introducing natural enemies. "It considers the pesticides as the ultimate weapon to be held in reserve until absolute necessity dictates its use. It is a sophisticated use of ecological principles. The fundamental aspect is that the program is based on a sophisticated understanding of the ecosystem involved."

Agricultural and biological scientists at several schools of the University of California system have become deeply involved in the pest control problem and the failure of chemicals, perhaps because California is undoubtedly the most heavily pesticided real estate in the world.

Paul DeBach, entomologist of the Citrus Research Center and Agricultural Experiment Station at Riverside: "Intensive ecological studies of the entire community complex, as well as of potential competitors and natural enemies, should precede all eradication programs against well-established pests except obviously necessary emergency programs."

Carl Huffaker, entomologist at Berkeley: "Properly viewed, pest control is basically a question of applied ecology; yet its practice has long been conducted with little regard to real necessity for control, in some cases, various deterimental side-effects or long-term advantage with respect even to the specific crop itself."

Robert Rudd, author of *Pesticides and the Living Landscape* and zoologist at Davis: "The ecological specialist has yet to—but must—become the primary recommending source for all problems of biological management. Environmental polutants from whatever source—automobiles, mistblowers, sewers, industrial manufacture—can and do produce ecological hazards. The ultimate risk of a degraded environment is the loss of biological productivity. No country can afford such a loss."

In a tacit acknowledgment of the Agriculture Department's inability to safeguard environment, the pesticide registration program was taken from its jurisdiction to be given to the new Environmental Protection Agency.

This discussion of modern agriculture has dealt largely with means. The end that agriculture has single-mindedly pursued is elimination of the ancient scourge of mankind, starvation. That this goal is being realized is a testament to human ingenuity. It is one of the species' truly heroic achievements. Unfortunately, while single-mindedness is a virtue in solving a target problem, it can become a vice within the larger ecological context. And, as we have seen before, while the analytic attack is supremely effective within the restricted one-problem one-solution framework, it can be maddeningly ineffectual in the complex situation that requires a holistic approach.

"In the long term," said ecologist Garrett Hardin, "we can't conquer famine with food." We have always seen that larger agricultural yields are followed by bumper crops of humans.

CHAPTER ELEVEN

Will Success Spoil Homo Sapiens?

1

IN BIBLICAL TIMES, the apocalyptic John beheld four horsemen: "And power was given unto them over the fourth part of the earth; to kill with sword, and with hunger, and with death, and with the beasts of the earth." If for death, the pale rider, we substitute disease, we have war, famine, disease, and predation. Lions still lived in Biblical Palestine, but fear of predators was a vestigial emotion. The species already had outgrown that threat.

Except for some cultural evolution, the situation remained unchanged until the time of Thomas Malthus at the turn of the 19th century. "The vices of mankind are active and able ministers of depopulation," Malthus wrote in his famous essay on population. "They are the precursors in the great army of destruction; and often finish the dreadful work themselves." These vices, which included poverty, might be summed up under the heading of man's inhumanity to man. War was an organized expression of this vice. "But should they fail in this war of extermination, sickly seasons, epidemics, pestilence, and plague advance in terrific array, and sweep off their thousands and ten thousands. Should success be still incomplete, gigantic inevitable

241

famine stalks in the rear, and with one mighty blow, levels the population with the food of the world."

Early in the 20th century, Vicente Blasco-Ibáñez wrote a novel of World War One followed by a motion picture that caught the popular imagination, *The Four Horsemen of the Apocalypse*. This time the horsemen were Flood, Famine, War, and Pestilence.

But even then—although men could not block the great tsunami tidal waves of the Pacific Ocean—humans to a great extent had controlled floods and any other over-whelming physical-environmental threat to the species. Men were in the process of stocking the armory of modern medi-cine with the weapons that would blunt the onslaught of disease. The influenza pandemic of 1918 was the last great world-wide pestilence. Finally, now, because of some of those weapons and control of plant species, famine too was falling behind.

Of all those once indomitable forces, only war—the threat of intraspecific destruction—rode at humanity's heels.

Today, man stands rampant on the field of nature, van-quisher of his old external enemies, demonstrating that mastery of environment which Aristotle took to be the evolutionary aim. There still are some problem areas, to be sure. Ten thousand humans a day die from starvation or malnutrition-related diseases. But increasing food produc-tion should overcome the maldistribution or even Mal-thusian "vices" which cause the misery.

Jean Mayer, a population expert and professor of nutri-tion at Harvard Universtiy, told Congress in September, 1969, "By 1952–53, the worldwide rate of per capita production of food had overtaken prewar rates. Since then, the average rate of increase in the production of food for the world at large has been three per cent per year while the population has increased on the average 1.7 per cent. Actually, this slight but steady gain of food production over population is part of a secular trend. E. S. and W. S. Woytinski, in their monumental *World Population and Production,* estimate that since 1850 the increase in output has been more rapid than the increase in population."

This does not yet reflect the Green Revolution. And just beginning is still another food revolution with as yet incalculable potential for human destiny. Laboratory-produced high-protein foods, such as spun soybean fiber—an imitation of meat—and synthetic amino acids already are entering the humin diet. Ahead are such factory-engineered products as alfalfa extract, fish protein concentrate, and cultured algae. SC—Single Cell Protein, produced in the basement of a Long Island laboratory, is being tested on animals. These micro-organisms are able to convert one pound of waste material—such as crude oil, methane gas, or old newspapers—into one pound of cells or one-half pound of pure protein. Two dozen petroleum companies are working on similar processes. The miniaturization in the acreage and technology required to produce a pound of SCP compared to a pound of steak possesses staggering implications.

Today's central problem goes back to Malthus. How could he have seemed to be so irrefutably right and yet proved so wrong? He said that population, when unchecked, grows geometrically. Subsistence increases only by arithmetic ratio and this discrepancy is what keeps population in check. And yet we find that subsistence is keeping ahead of population.

In "Toward a Non-Malthusian Population Policy," Jean Mayer writes, "I hope I have said enough to show how dangerous it may turn out to link the population problem so closely to food, as so many writers have done. These have generally been conservationists and social scientists rather than agricultural or nutritional scientists, concerned—rightly—with the effects of crowding which they have observed. At the same time, not sure that the public and governments would agree with them that there was cause for concern, and action, based on these grounds, they have turned to the threat of a worldwide shortage of food as an easily understood, imperative reason for a large-scale limitation of births."

Disease, Malthus's other check on population, itself has been checked. Even the Malthusian vice, poverty, is not as much of a problem today as is affluence, Dr. Mayer points out, with its exorbitant demands on resources and environment.

But when investigators have turned to resources, they have been confronted by still another Alice in Wonderland paradox. While the earth is finite and its resources obviously limited, still man has demonstrated an amazing ability to expand resources even as he was consuming materials at ever greater rates. In this regard, the description of resources by geographer John Chapman is pertinent: "In the human ecosystem, man assigns utility to various elements of his environment and thus confers upon them the role of resources. Resources then are neither wholly of the physical world nor wholly of the world of man but are the result of the interaction between the two."

The cry of wolf at the door of resources has tended further to discredit advocates of conservation; in actuality more use has led to more production in an ever-expanding economy. Harold Barnett and Chandler Morse in *Scarcity and Growth: The Economics of Natural Resource Availability* wrote that the conservation movement's "sense of impending scarcity" dates back to 1877 when Carl Schurz, as Secretary of the Interior, forecast a timber famine with enough supplies to last only another 20 years. Hans Landsberg of Resources for the Future says that when estimates were made in 1962 timber growth exceeded cut by 60 percent.

Gifford Pinchot in *The Fight for Conservation* after the turn of the century raised similar cries about coal, iron, mineral oil, and natural gas as well as timber. But, says economist Landsberg, look what happened, in the case of coal, for example. The average American of 1966 used only about half the amount of coal as did his forebear of 1910. "The decline was not, however, motivated by thrift or evidence of waste, as the conservation movement understood these terms. Rather, the prime reasons were vastly greater efficiency in burning, especially in steam-electric plants, and the emergence of other energy sources . . ."

Despite the fact that the amount of coal ultimately is limited, Hans Landsberg points out, the Interior Department has spent millions of dollars on research into ways not to conserve coal but to find new uses for it. This alteration in attitude has been brought about, he says, by the impact of increased knowledge and improved technology. "We have enhanced our ability to upgrade old resources (for example, cropland through the addition of fertilizer), to discover new ones (oil, gas, nuclear fission, and so forth), to utilize them more efficiently (coal in power generation, low-grade copper ore, wood waste for pulp mills and building board, and the like), and to adjust to relative resource availabilities (aluminum replacing copper, or air-cooling replacing water-cooling). Consequently, the relative importance of the country's resources as inputs into the economic hopper has steadily diminished."

The resource of space obviously poses an ultimate check

on population—Philip Hauser, director of the University of Chicago's Population Research Center, calculated that if world population keeps increasing at its current rate, in six and a half centuries population densities would reach one person per square foot. But short of such saturation, density as a check on human population is difficult to assess. Thirty million Americans are crowded into the 14,000 square miles of megalopolis between Boston and Washington—more than 2,000 per square mile, high as human concentrations go for such a sizable area. However, as Dr. Lawrence Hinkle, Jr., head of the Human Ecology Division of Cornell Medical College, observes, modern man thrives in this environment. The median family income in this region is one thousand dollars a year more than in the rest of the United States. Is this area overpopulated? If so, then greater population density lies ahead. By 1985, 71 percent of all Americans are expected to live in metropolitan areas, an increase of 58 percent over 1960.

Then is the Malthusian doctrine overthrown? The answer is no. The human race is busily confirming the dismal theorem of the Reverend Malthus that population, when unchecked, invariably increases. Provide the subsistence and other requisite resources, remove predation, reduce disease and other controls, and *Homo sapiens* is doing exactly what any other species would do under the circumstances.

For three centuries the human population has been growing at an ever accelerating rate.

Dr. Mayer sees the sufficiency of food as far from an encouraging factor. "If anything, this view makes me even more pessimistic about our chances of limiting the world's population at an early date: famine or the threat of famine is perhaps the worst method of limitation, but it would work."

2

The human population figures and awesome projections have been given in many forums, but it is necessary to present some of the statistics in order to convey the magnitude and nature of the problem.

Our generation and the next are victims of compound interest, the phenomenon of the whole doubling through the addition of steady increments. To go back to the illustration of the bacteria with the capacity to divide by mitosis and thus double the population every 20 minutes. Let us say a colony of 100 bacteria starts in a medium with sufficient space and nutriment to support a population of 100 billion with no other limiting factors. In 10 hours, the bacteria have achieved maximum supportable population size. After 10 hours, the bacteria colony still is proceeding normally, everything going well. At 10 hours and 20 minutes, there are 200 billion bacteria, and the population collapses. If the process is extended in a science fiction fantasy, as R. H. MacArthur and J. H. Connell calculated, the colony would cover the surface of the earth to a height of one foot in 36 hours, and just one hour after that would be over our heads. Such is the power of exponential growth. The *rate* of increase doesn't change. But the ever-growing base builds to a critical proprrortion so that at some point a final doubling produces an insupportable biomass.

In human population, not only is the base expanding, but the rate of increase is accelerating. It took one million years or so to produce some five million humans by the dawn of agriculture 10,000 years ago. By the time of Christ, there were some 130 million humans, a doubling time for the population of about 1,800 years. By 1650, the doubling time had been cut in half and the population was 500 million. It took only 180 years to redouble to one billion individuals in 1830. Doubling time dropped to a century, and there were two billion people in 1930. Again a reduction in doubling time to 45 years with four billion people projected for 1975. The present world doubling rate is about 35 years.

Even without an accelerated growth rate, the persistent doubling of the base still means a rendezvous with an unacceptable total. The United States growth rate has been declining. "In the United States of America," Malthus cited as his example, "where means of subsistence have been more ample, the manners of the people more pure, and consequently the checks to early marriages fewer than in any of the modern states of Europe, the population has been found to double itself in twenty-five years." Today, the U.S. population is doubling once every 70 years—a growth rate of about one percent—but now the base is some 200 million people so that there will be 300 million Americans in 2000, 400 million in 2040, and so on.

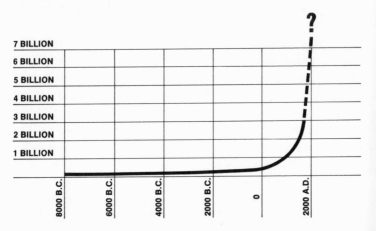

WORLD POPULATION GROWTH CURVE

On a world scale, the growth rate is two percent, hence a doubling time of only 35 years—that means seven billion humans by the years 2000 with one billion additional humans *every five years*. Every decade, an increment of population as large as all the human numbers in 1930! If civilization with its prodigies of production can accommodate the additional numbers, can it do so at that pace? Relentlessly? If the answer still is yes, are all these humans desirable?

Projections can change, of course, but barring nuclear war or some cataclysm, the human population course to a large extent already is set until the end of the century. All the world's mothers for the next 20 years already have been born. In 1940, there were 32 million American women of childbearing age. In 1950, 34 million; in 1960, 36 million; in 1970, 43 million; and in 1980, there will be 54 million. Even with the most realistic contraction of the birth rate, the American population could be no less than 280 million.

This is the population time bomb, the bomb about which Dr. Paul Ehrlich has written and spoken. It shows why such a long lead time is required in population planning and why calamity in this area cannot be avoided on short notice.

As we have seen, growth rate is determined by four factors—natality, mortality, emigration, and immigration. On a world scale, the last two factors are inoperative since no one is emigrating to other worlds and none of our species is flying in from somewhere else. The modern acceleration of the growth rate has been caused by a reduction in mortality, largely among the infant and older age categories. This change is reflected in our longer life expectancy: 33 years in the United States in 1900, about 71 years today.

As in other animal species, human natality tends to adjust to mortality. Demographers have calculated that in order to achieve the American growth rate of the early

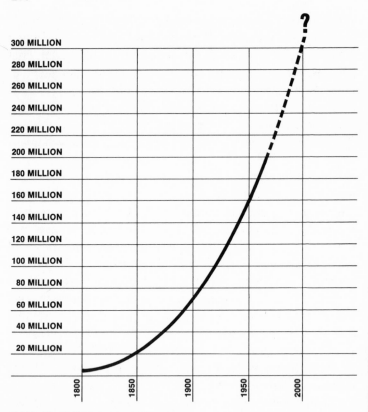

UNITED STATES POPULATION

1800s, each woman averaged close to eight and a half births. Today that average is down to two and a half offspring. In Asian, African, and Latin American countries where improved medical, sanitation, and subsistence methods have drastically cut the death rate, natality still has not had time to adjust. The result of the dislocation is a soaring growth rate. In Costa Rica, for example, the growth rate is more than 3½ percent, meaning that nation's population will double in less than 20 years. Not a matter of concern perhaps in a country of about one and a half millions. But in India with a population of more than half a billion, the doubling rate is 28 years.

Many countries of Europe have come close to stabilizing their populations. According to Population Reference Bureau figures for 1968, Belgium, Luxembourg, East Germany, and Hungary all had growth rates of less than four-tenths of one percent or population doubling times of close to two centuries or more. Nevertheless, the population of *every* nation on earth is expanding.

If birth rate exceeds death rate, the result in the world population is a positive growth rate; if mortality exceeds natality, the result is a minus growth rate; if natality and mortality are equal, the result is zero growth rate and eventually a stable population. It can be seen from these simple equations that the price of every medical breakthrough prolonging life or reducing mortality is either an accelerated growth rate or a further decrease in natality.

One way to bring the two factors into balance is to increase mortality. If nuclear war is an unpalatable not to say hazardous remedy, it is equally difficult to visualize any politician running, and being elected, on a platform of free euthanasia.

This leaves as the other alternative reduction of input. Contrary to popular impression, there are effective methods of birth control other than "the pill." Ireland and other European countries have achieved close to stable populations by customarily marrying late in adulthood and through emigration—exporting potential parents. Spacing children over long intervals in a marriage produces hard-to-believe reduction in the total population.

To go back to the example of the African elephants that

turned to spacing as a population-control mechanism. The female in the low density area that began breeding at 12 years and then had an offspring every seven years averages six offspring in a lifetime. In the high density compound, breeding did not start until age 20 and then recurred every 12 years. This cut reproduction in half and reduced the population by two-thirds.

Another example of this population geometry: A human female who reproduces at about top capacity is born in 1900, has her first child at 15, and thereafter gives birth to one offspring a year for her childbearing career. In 1945, she has 30 children, all daughters who are efficient breeders. The first daughter starts to reproduce at the age of 15 in 1930, the second daughter in 1931, and so on. By 1950, that family has about 300 members. If the first daughter were lost—just that one—the family would number about 245.

In the United States, population growth has been propelled by four pressures, all of which have intensified since World War Two. Lincoln Day of Yale University lists them as low death rate, nearly universal marriage, marriage at an early age, and clustering of family size between two and four children. It can be seen that three of these factors are strongly influenced by social pressures. "Human societies," says Judith Blake Davis of the University of California's Department of Demography, "are organized so as to encourage, even exert strong pressures on, their members to marry and reproduce." Women have been offered few viable options for careers except as wives and mothers, the unmarried must endure pity or suspicion. Income taxes favor the fecund, school taxes discriminate against the abstinent. (If parents were made to bear the full costs of all "externalities," there would be greater resort to fertility control.) But until recently, all states enforced compulsory pregnancy by making abortions illegal (Japan with legalized abortion accomplished a spectacular reduction in its post-war birth rate).

Even with the pill, diaphragm, condom, and interuterine device, planned parenthood is based upon how many children the couple *wants*. No consideration is given to how many children society *needs*. If a wealthy couple has many children, people say, "Oh, they can afford them." Nobody asks if society can afford them. "Perhaps the most dangerous element in the present situation," President Nixon told Congress on July 18, 1969, in his message "Problems of Population Growth," "is the fact that so few people are examining these questions from the viewpoint of the whole society."

With this all said, there are deep biological urges to reproduce, reflecting the age-old evolutionary pressure of survival. And while too many unwanted children enter the world, most children are wanted. Nature has made the young, of most mammalian species for that matter, seductively appealing. The joy of having children is one of the few pure gifts of life. The abnegation and circumscription of existence itself for many people in limiting their family to two children—necessary for a stable population—are immeasurable. For them, it is a cruel dilemma.

Therefore, is expanding population injurious to human life? Or will it be? Is there a problem of overpopulation? Or will there be?

3

You would have to look hard to find an economist who will come out four-square against growth, of any kind. Recall former Presidential adviser Walter Heller saying he could not conceive of a successful economy without growth. In March, 1970, Hendrick Houthakker, a member of the President's Council of Economic Advisers, said, "There is little reason to expect overpopulation for the world as a whole in the foreseeable future. Most serious studies of the subject suggest that the food supply can be expanded to accommodate a much larger population than now exists on earth." There might be a shortage of some minerals, he said, but they could be compensated for through substitution. "What is of course more serious is that overpopulation may lead to a degradation of the social and physical environment, but this appears to be more a matter of the proper distribution of the population than of total numbers. Much can be done to improve the environment without attempting to influence population trends."

Ecologists take a diametrically opposed position. They say the human population is out of control, posing a highly dangerous situation. Crawford Holling believes the human population "has all the attributes of a bacterial colony during the first few moments of growth." Marston Bates compares the behavior of the human population to a cancer. The population problem, says George Woodwell, underlies all our other problems. Continued population growth means inevitable erosion of the present American standard of living. And, magnified by technology (our technology also is out of control, Dr. Woodwell says), overpopulation degrades environment. The twin effects of continued population growth are: deterioration of the human environment and of the quality of human life.

Demographers—social scientists who specialize in the study of the human population—are somewhere between the ecologists and the economists. Most tend to agree with ecologists that growth must be curbed and population stabilized, but some demographers decry ecologists' "alarmist" warnings. Philip Hauser scoffed at what he termed the efforts of "angry ecologists" and "Johnny-come-lately's" to scare the nation into cleaning up the environment and slowing American population growth. Dr. Hauser told an American Medical Association Congress in May, 1970, "There are an awful lot of people who will survive the 1970's and then conclude that all this is buncombe."

Joseph Fisher, president of Resources for the Future and an economist, took a similar attitude toward ecologists' viewing with alarm. Speaking before a House Subcommittee considering the effects of population growth on natural resources and environment, Dr. Fisher said, "I would warn my colleagues and the committee not too quickly to assume you can build a case for population planning and limitation for this country during the next few decades simply on an overwhelming deleterious effect on the natural environment. I think there is a great danger of the oversell from ecologists and the conservationists, of whom I am one, and it will not go with the American people just by asserting it because they are checking against their ordinary experience and they are thinking things are not all that bad."

At the same hearing, Garrett Hardin told the House Operations Subcommittee: "I am usually called an ecologist, and some economist has rightfully remarked that ecology is now the dismal science. It has replaced economics." That might be a measure of how much the one science has disavowed Malthus and the other has embraced him.

If ecologists are regarded as Cassandras, it would be well to remember who Cassandra was. She was the daughter of Priam, king of Troy. Cassandra prophesied the doom of Troy, but since that fortress city-state was obviously invulnerable to the long siege of the Greeks outside the walls on the plains below, nobody believed her. Troy fell in one night after the siege had been lifted, the Greeks apparently had departed, and the menace seemed ended.

"It is part of the essential character of most of the impending catastrophes," ecologist Kenneth Watt told the same Congressional panel, "that they will intensify suddenly, with little advance warning. It is noteworthy, as in the case of hurricane Camille, that where a catastrophe is predicted outside the range of human experience with little advance warning, many people do not accept the predictions."

Dr. Watt went on to tell the Congressmen, "The high cost per capita of services, education, and government is making even a very small rate of population increase intolerably burdensome to the taxpayers. We must stop population increase altogether. The United States would be a more salubrious environment for its citizens if the population was 100 million."

Roger Revelle, director of Harvard University's Center for Population Studies, believes that population must be stabilized, but he quickly took issue with ecologist Watt's population estimate. "I just do not understand the statement made by Dr. Watt that 100 million people would be the right number, the optimum population, for the United States. I do not know how to ask this question, what is the optimum population? There is no evidence one way or the other that I know of as to what the optimum population is."

This question—"Is There an Optimum Level of Population?"—was the subject of a symposium at an American Association for the Advancement of Science Meeting in December, 1969.

At that symposium, Preston Cloud, Jr., a biogeologist at the Universtiy of California, Santa Barbara, expressed belief that we already are overpopulated. "We are, in fact, deluged with evidence that, for current conditions, a world population of three and a half billion already exceeds the optimum, while more than 200 million inhabitants of the United States are also too many for its level of consumption, aspirations, and domestic resources."

Joseph Fisher of Resources for the Future disagreed with what he called Dr. Cloud's "pessimistic outlook." Dr. Fisher said that 300 million Americans by the year 2000 could have a better standard of living, although he would not make the same prediction for the rest of the world.

Harrison Brown, a geochemist with the California Institute of Technology, said he doesn't believe an industrial technological society is limited by availability of non-renewable resources. The gravest danger he foresaw was that if an advanced technological society were interrupted by some disaster, it would be unable to start up again.

Alvin Weinberg, director of the Oak Ridge National Laboratory, said that much more efficient "breeder" nuclear fission reactors which should be operative in 10 to 15 years could supply the energy requirements for a world population of 20 billion people. But the task would require 4,000 nuclear parks based near the oceans for cooling. Dr. Weinberg said he could not predict that material life for the individual would be downgraded with a population of 20 billion.

Barry Commoner said that the human population had escaped the controls of the ecosystem. He said that decline in the death rate always precedes decline in the birth rate and demographic transition to a stabilized population could not possibly take place for another 20 or 30 years even if we start reducing the growth rate immediately. So Dr. Commoner foresaw a certain human population of from six to eight billion people. He believed food could be supplied for these people, but such a population would dangerously stress the environment. "We are now entering the survival crisis," he said.

Chauncey Starr, dean of the School of Engineering at the University of California, Los Angeles, said that the global life cycle of contaminants is not understood well enough for predictive purposes. The population problem, he said, is not one of growth, but of concentration, and the population density of Hong Kong of about 10,000 people per square mile is as much as the environment can take.

S. Fred Singer of the Department of the Interior emphasized that "since the costs of achieving and maintaining environmental quality go up faster than the GNP, it follows that a larger and larger fraction has to be spent in order to maintain environmental quality. Wherever the fraction becomes unacceptable, it is at that point that we have passed the optimum level of population."

Director John Knowles of Massachusetts General Hospital said of optimum population from a public health point of view, "we have exceeded it, gentlemen—we have already exceeded it."

Geneticist Bentley Glass foresaw in a huge, homogeneous population and society's intention to use medicine to save everyone the deterioration of the species. Because of modern medicine, many more genetically flawed individuals are enabled to live beyond the age of reproduction; the result is an increase of detrimental genes in the human pool. Moreover, the interbreeding pool of a world community will be so gigantic that it will smother genetic variability and the evolutionary ability to exploit such diversity when needed for adaptive defenses. "The man of tomorrow," Dr. Glass said, "will clearly need many more pills and prosthetic devices. That need not worry us so long as the social cost is not too great and so long as we can maintain our artificial environment unimpaired. By natural standards we may become degenerate physical beings, but we will not wish to apply natural standards any more."

There is a way out for the species, Dr. Glass observed. "If in the end we blunder into a nuclear war and eliminate nine-tenths of the human lives on the planet," among those who survive the blast, the heat, the radiation, the subsequent fallout, the loss of drugs, pills, special foods, and medical devices—among those survivors "there will very likely be the high level of genetic diversity that will enable *Homo sapiens* to make a wiser fresh start."

4

The diversity most noticeable in this scientific symposium was of opinion. Not only was there no consensus, but few common denominators. Not only no common point of view toward the question, but no common basis for judgment. What emerges is a startling realization of the lack of competency of any individual scientific discipline to deal with the most momentous of contemporary questions: what is human overpopulation, when is human overpopulation?

With one exception.

As we have seen, the study of natural populations has been a central concern of ecology. As we have seen, ecology does offer a yardstick by which to measure, models by which to compare, standards by which to judge.

In nature, we have myriad examples of what we must infer to be optimum populations since they are the rule. The optimum population is the population needed to make full and efficient use of available resources and permitted by the most restrictive limiting factor. Most natural populations exist in equilibrium with their environment, thus a stable population continues until an environment change causes an adjustment.

Some populations are exceptions to this rule of equilibrium. Some insect or microbial populations are unresponsive to environmental signals and continue to multiply. Or the resource availability may vary—for example, the cyclic abundance of snowshoe hares for the Canadian lynxes or the growth of a crop that is suddenly removed by harvesting. Or extraordinary conditions may supervene such as systematic removal of predators of the deer on the Kaibab plateau. In any of these cases, the population exceeds the size that can be supported by available resources or violates some limiting factor. The excess always proves to be temporary. The demands of reality recall the runaway population to supportable dimensions. The return usually is as precipitous as the ascent. Thus if a population rockets past the supportable level with the full force of exponential growth, the quickly developing imbalance must be redressed in haste and a population "crash" results.

From this behavior of non-human populations has come the concept of carrying capacity—the intrinsic capacity of a habitat, the sum of all available resources, to support a population of a certain size. In the graphic description of populations, this carrying capacity is designated as the upper asymptote. How the population reacts to this environmental barrier is reflected in the growth curve, the normal sigmoidal S curve showing a flattening to come into conformity with carrying capacity, the irresponsive J overshooting the upper asymptote and heralding a sharp decline in the population (see diagram of Population Growth Curves, p. 106).

In nature, it is a relatively simple matter to discover the carrying capacity for a particular population—just observe what exists or, in a new population, wait to see what develops. The reproductive force will always push a biological population to this environmental barrier or beyond, with resultant oscillations or fluctuations around the upper asymptote.

This upper level is not necessarily a static line. As ecologists have found, natural populations can affect their environment—alter its carrying capacity—as well as being affected by it. A plague of locusts eating everything in sight is one example of reducing carrying capacity. Beavers gnaw down trees, build dams, and form ponds in order to create an environment favorable to more beavers. The forest modifies its surroundings in order to shape an environment most conducive to perpetuation of the forest.

Man is the most successful species in exploiting resources and modifying environment to enhance its carrying capacity. To look at it another way, he keeps pushing back limiting factors as he comes to them. To some observers, *Homo sapiens* is so successful that they can see no limit to the species' growth. Man seems to have slipped the bonds that confine other species.

The role of the ecologist is to ask instead whether *Homo sapiens* has severed its sensors to reality, removed the vital links that guide other populations into compatible equilibrium with their environment. Ecologist Holling:

"When both the population and the environmental capacity are growing by some kind of law, it is possible to show that the signal generated by the environmental limit to the population may be extremely weak. Not only is the signal weak, but it is difficult to track. Hence a biologically unique situation emerges. World population and the institutions that serve man can operate as if there were no signal from the environment saying that the world is limited."

Ecologists are sure of two things. One is that you never

get something for nothing. Each human being needs some 2,000 calories of food energy per day in order to live, 3,000 in order to live well. Man gets this supply from contemporary solar energy transmuted by plant photosynthesis, as do all other species. But this is only about one percent of all energy being consumed in the United States, the rest going to produce electricity, fuel autos, and do the work that maintains the high-level civilization. This energy comes mainly from solar energy previously sequestered and stored in fossel fuels supplemented by nuclear energy.

Americans have access to such a profusion of energy— ubiquitous electricity for their toothbrushes and pencil sharpeners, fuel for their lawn mowers and minibikes, batteries for their tape recorders and plastic toys, lighter fluid to speed their barbecues and ease the starting of campfires— that energy seems if not limitless then certainly too lavish for any exact accounting. But in fact, the ledger for the American civilization is kept very strictly. Loss of a major fossil fuel supply would translate very quickly to a reduced standard of living—inconvenience, deprivation, physical hardship, and perhaps worse.

The United States has about 6 percent of the world's population and uses about 40 percent of its produced natural resources. This multiplication of individuals by consumption in effect produces a very much larger population. In terms of energy use, the present American population is equivalent to 20 *billion* of the original native inhabitants. And while we are accustomed to thinking of the population on the subcontinent of India as very large, still in terms of population-electrical energy there are 35 times as many Americans.

Therefore, it should not be surprising that the large-scale impact of population-consumption upon environment first became manifest in the United States. Pollution and deterioration of habitat are signs of overpopulation in other species. Poisonous wastes frequently are the limiting factor in the growth of fast-multiplying bacteria and other organisms. Overpopulation of the Kaibab deer degraded the habitat to such an extent that it was able to support only a reduced population on a continuing basis.

The magnification of population by consumption has a second significance; it bears the same relationship as the equivalently larger population to carrying capacity. Biogeologist Preston Cloud defines this relationship as "the product of population times per capita consumption of goods and amenities divided into total resources available." Because of a relatively small population on a large land area, because of huge food production, and because of its advanced civilization, the United States appears to be well-buffered from any effects of world-wide overpopulation. But the U.S. civilization depends on high consumption of nonrenewable resources, and just about everybody's consumption of these resources is increasing exponentially along with population. The United States is self-sufficient only in magnesium, molybdenum, and a few other metals; it imports most of its bauxite, chrome, tin, and cobalt; extensively supplements its lead, zinc, and tungsten; and its dependence is growing upon foreign petroleum, iron, and copper.

That population-consumption cannot increase indefinitely is the second thing of which ecologists are certain. *Every* population either stabilizes or reaches a zenith and falls. The operative questions for the human population are not will it stabilize, but when, in what manner, by what means, at what level? "I hope it is by plan," says George Woodwell, thinking of the harsh measures employed on

other natural populations. These, then, are the basic considerations in the conversion—that it doesn't come about in an
unpleasant way or at a level of population where people no
longer enjoy their life and environment.

But in order to determine that, we must discover the
missing factor in the demographic equation—the carrying
capacity for *Homo sapiens*. In order to know whether the
human growth curve is a J with its implicit population crash
or whether there still is room for a graceful transition into
equilibrium with environment, we must know the level of
the upper asymptote. Is human population overshooting its
carrying capacity or is there still room?

5

As it happens, the National Academy of Sciences ap-
pointed a blue-ribbon Committee on Resources and Man to
undertake such a monumental assay—"to evaluate national
and world resources in the light of current and expected
stresses . . ." While acknowledging the indispensibility of
pure air and water to human survival, the report concentrates on other, non-renewable resources. The findings of
the panel of eight scientists drawing on the help of about
eighty colleagues were published in December, 1969, as the
volume *Resources and Man*. It must be considered our most
current authoritative assessment of the state of *Homo sapiens* with relation to environment. The problem is ap-
proached with the ecological view, attacked with the tools
of ecology, and judged by ecological concepts and values.

In explaining the rationale of the approach and evalua-
tion, the introduction states:

"A prime conclusion of ecology is that species whose
populations exceed or approach too closely the carrying

capacity of resources in the space occupied undergo reduction. Such reductions are often severe and may lead to
extinction because of disease, pestilence, predation, or aggressive competitors. Although it is true that man has repeatedly succeeded in increasing both the space he occupies
and its carrying capacity, and that he will continue to do so,
it is also clear that both the occupiable space and its carrying capacity have finite limits which he can approach only
at great peril."

The report suggests how perilously close the human race
is to this fateful rendezvous.

Some of the many findings are:

Probably three-quarters of the floors of the ocean basins
contain little mineral wealth.

The probable ultimate sustained food production from
the oceans is not likely to be more than two and a half times
the present annual production of 60 million metric tons of
fish.

We are approaching so close to the limits of mineral
stocks that "it is not certain whether, in the next century or
two, further industrial development based on mineral resources will be foreclosed by limitations of supply. The
biggest unknowns are population and rates of consumption."

Helium is in extremely short supply; so are tin, tungsten,
and mercury. The price of mercury has increased 500 percent during the past 20 years; even so, it is unlikely that
United States production will last another generation. This
is a particularly interesting situation since, in the spring and
summer of 1970, investigators found highly toxic mercury
pollution from industrial wastes in Lake Erie, Lake Cham-
plain, and the waterways of a dozen Eastern states. The
metal still was not scarce enough for prodigal American
industry to bother to conserve it!

As for mineral fuels, the bulk of the crude oil and natural gas will be consumed in another 50 years, but liquid fuels from tar sands and oil shales may extend the lifetime of the petroleum family to a century. This, the major energy source for Western civilization and for the newly converted industrialized agriculture! There is enough coal in the world to last three to four centuries, but only one to two centuries if used as the main energy source.

Of other major energy sources, solar energy obviously has the most potential, but it is technologically unpromising. Man's options as an adequate replacement for the fossil fuels are reduced to one—nuclear power.

At present, so-called light-water fission reactors already are in operation and many more are being built. But these power plants can use only the fissionable isotope uranium-235, and this constitutes less than one percent of the uranium supply. U-235 as a principal energy source can last only until about the end of the century. A second generation "breeder" reactor can use nonfissionable uranium-238, which comprises more than 99 percent of natural uranium, and thorium-232, which makes up most of the natural thorium. These fuel supplies would last several thousand years —the thorium in the granite quarries of Vermont alone would last for five centuries.

Beyond breeder reactors is thermonuclear fusion. The supply of its fuel, the deuterium in the oceans, may be considered sufficient for the duration of the species. But controlled atomic fusion has not been achieved, and there is no guarantee it ever will be. Of course, an upper limit to nuclear energy may be imposed by radiation, thermal pollution, or atomic waste disposal.

There is another problem with the fission breeder reactors; they must go into operation before the supply of fissionable U-235 runs out, because it is essential to start the breeder fission process. The breeder reactors should be ready in 10 to 15 years to take over from the present light-water reactors. In one of the most chilling matter-of-fact sentences in print, M. King Hubbert writes in the energy chapter in *Resources and Man*, "Failure to make this transition would constitute one of the major disasters in human history." It's that close.

Finally, it is estimated that by cultivating all arable land, attaining maximum productivity, with new crops and the use of more vegetable protein and including the increased food production from oceans, food supplies could be increased nine times the present amount.

That puts the earth's ultimate carrying capacity at 30 billion people "at a level of chronic near-starvation for the great majority." The report points out that this figure is little more than three doublings of population and could be achieved in about one century.

But if people are to live well, anywhere near their rising expectations, the report goes on, effort must be made to stabilize populations at a world level much lower than 10 billion. "Indeed it is our judgment that a human population less than the present one would offer the best hope for comfortable living for our descendants, long duration for the species, and the preservation of environmental quality."

The "inescapable" central conclusion of the report is that both population control and better resource management are mandatory and should begin at once. "To delay progress toward full self-regulation of population size is to play 'Russian roulette' with the future of man."

It seems that the most exceptional and successful of all species must make still one more exception in order to preserve the success. *Homo sapiens* must refute Malthus. Humanity must go against the entire biological evolutionary tide and control its numbers voluntarily.

Extrication from this human predicament appears at least possible because of the intelligence for which man named himself—intelligence to conceptualize contingent futures.

If humanity falters, it may be overtaken by four phantom horsemen still riding at its heels. Only their names now are Population, Pollution, War, and Consumption—not the invisible White Plague of the 19th century, but the conspicuous consumption of the 20th.

CHAPTER TWELVE

Perspective

IN THIS AGE OF REVOLUTION and rumors of revolution, noisy rebellions and self-proclaimed revolutionaries, the one authentic revolution proceeds unappreciated for what it is. Ecology combines the fervor of a new philosophy or religion with the cold force of science. Like philosophy or religion, ecology offers revealed truth, but it is not so ambitious as to lay claim to ultimate reality. It is content with the reality amenable to science. It was content to incorporate into its truth that part of reality eschewed by other sciences, the environment, a part of reality against which ecological truths can be tested by the senses of every man.

Ecology's assertion of reality—like the idea whose time has come—sweeps onward with irresistible power. See what it already has accomplished.

Ecology challenges the autonomy of applied chemistry. It insists that chemists stop behaving like irresponsible little boys with their chemistry sets indiscriminately spewing poisons into the environment. It suggests that chemists determine beforehand the ecological consequences of their chemicals, which would seem to put some chemists in an untenable position. Ecology bids physicists to adopt a similar responsibility for consequences, encouraging them to consider the biological flesh as well as the physical skeleton.

While the ecological challenge is theoretical or intellectual, the effects can be quite tangible. At the same time, the niche of ecology is so broad that it touches all men's activities. The creation by Congress of National Environmental Policy Law and the sweeping revision by the President of powers once held by various Cabinet departments into an Environmental Protection Agency ordains great changes in the way American governmental agencies, companies, and other institutions behave. Ecology challenges the widely held assumption that tinkering with environment is good *per se*, that man can always improve upon nature. This challenge could undermine a great part of the perpetual make-work program of the U.S. Army Corps of Engineers which, if not discouraged, will always find another river to dam, another stream to straighten, another canal to cut, another estuary to dredge.

The frontal clash with the Lewis Carroll view of reality espoused by economists could defrock them as the high priests of our society. Economists might escape such a fate by admitting more data into their restricted representation of reality; the move to recognize "externalities" seems to be a start toward such an accommodation. In the end, economists may save themselves by becoming ecologists.

The social role ecology will play seems just beginning. The 26th and final recommendation made by the NAS Committee on Resources and Man—the only recommendation made under the heading of Organization—calls for setting up in the Federal Government "a high-level group of broadly qualified resource specialists and ecologists." Among their recommended duties are "achievement of maximum social well being and international harmony in the uses of resources."

Already ecology has provided society with compelling reasons why it must not allow its hunters to exterminate mountain lions, wolves, and blue whales. It has instructed well-meaning public health officials that if they intend to decrease mortality, they must entertain ways to reduce natality as well. It has reminded agriculture that man does not live by food alone. And it asks religions: what does it profit a man to save his own soul and lose the whole world?

Is any human institution safe from ecology? "When I think of the 80 billion dollars going for military expenditures!" says George Woodwell, "That's what men were doing three thousand years ago, we haven't come any farther—and we have such fantastic problems to solve."

"We're not going to make it if we persist in fighting major wars, throwing away our energies," says David Gates. "Priorities—it always comes back to that. We have to learn to care about what kind of environment we're going to live in. The question is, Will we learn in time?"

At the dedication ceremonies of Redwood National Park in November, 1968, California's State Secretary of Natural Resources, Norman Livermore, Jr., said, "We trust that following this major purchase of superlative redwoods by the Federal Government, there will be no further acquisition that would withdraw from production substantial acreage of redwood producing lands that are essential to maintain the local economy." Timber men, strip miners, oil drillers, and agriculturists see the land as a supply depot. But it is much more than that. It is the *oikos*, our home. It is what shapes us. We are part of it, literally.

Perhaps the Ecological Revolution is so deceptive because until the recent past it seemed to have been preoccupied with matters of minor importance in the affairs of men. But its revolutionary import is contained in the redefining of man's image of himself and of his role in the world. Man is the only creature who has learned how the system works. And so he has tried to run the system to suit his exclusive needs and wants. This was perfectly natural. Any species would do the same thing. From this, man has come to see himself as king. And he seemed to have the power of knowledge to enforce his commands.

Now comes ecology, saying first, that the system is far more complicated than men originally thought. How can you run the system if you don't completely understand it? Second, even if man gleans the last scintilla of information, he will never be absolute master of the system because he is a part of it, not apart from it.

Ecology says that man is not king despite his illusions. He must give up the imagined scepter. He must obey certain ecological rules and *will* heed them.

Continued disregard of these laws will probably not bring extinction to the species. Ecologists are not so much prophets of death as seers of a worse fate. Refusal to exist in equilibrium with the environment means debasing man's habitat; improvident use of resources impoverishes posterity. Man must limit his numbers or relinquish individual freedom. He must protect the ecosystem or pollute himself, preserve nature's diversity or live with monotony, respect nature's frontiers or sentence himself to a world-wide prison.

So these ecological laws are not absolutes. They come down to a series of priorities. They allow for the operation of the free will that *Homo sapiens* won after such an arduous struggle. But the choices also impose a responsibility upon every thinking human, a responsibility that can be neither shirked nor avoided, for the decisions are being made now. This responsibility is the burden that man has assumed along with the power and freedom.

Man should be able to change. In addition to intelligence, adaptability has been his other saving trait.

The initial achievements of ecology—its insights into the natural world, its new perspective—offer a rational basis for optimism for the future of *Homo sapiens*. And if we start applying the wisdom of ecology, perhaps there will be a synergistic effect, an unanticipated side effect: an improved society, what political leaders call a better world.

Whatever happens, it was through ecology that men first discerned the outlines of incipient hell.

References

CHAPTER ONE. *The Wedding of Ecology and Survival*

1. Kenneth Auchincloss, "An Early Warning System for Happenings in Nature," *The New York Times Magazine* (April 12, 1970).
2. Smithsonian Institution for Short-Lived Phenomena, *1969 Annual Report.*
3. Richard H. Chesher, *"Acanthaster planci*: Impact on Pacific Coral Reefs," Westinghouse Research Laboratories, Pittsburgh, Pa., October 15, 1969.
4. Eugene P. Odum, *Fundamentals of Ecology* (Philadelphia: Saunders, 1959).
5. James A. Sugar, "Starfish Threaten Pacific Reefs," *National Geographic* (March, 1970).
6. "Battle of Coral Sea," *Newsweek* (July 14, 1969).
7. "War on Starfish in the Pacific Is Urged to Save Coral Reefs," *The New York Times* (December 10, 1969).
8. *Sea Secrets*, vol. 13, no. 11 (December, 1969).
9. Peter Farb, *Ecology* (New York: Time, Inc., 1963).
10. "What Are We Doing to Our World, Part I," *The 21st Century*, broadcast over CBS Television Network, March 16, 1969.
11. Kenneth E. F. Watt, "A Comparative Study on the Meaning of Stability in Five Biological Systems: Insect and Furbearer Populations, Influenza, Thai Hemorrhagic Fever, and Plague," Brookhaven Symposia in Biology, no. 22, *Diversity and Stability in Ecological Systems* (May, 1969).

12. Dragoslav Ninkovich and Bruce C. Heezen, "Santorini Tephra," Proceedings of the 17th Symposium of the Colston Research Society, April 5–9, 1965.

13. LaMont Cole, "Can the World Be Saved?" *The New York Times Magazine* (March 31, 1968).

14. *Time Magazine* (February 2, 1970).

15. Edward J. Kormondy, *Concepts of Ecology* (Englewood Cliffs, N.J.: Prentice-Hall, 1969).

16. Charles Elton, *Animal Ecology* (London: Methuen, Science Paperbacks, 1927).

17. Arthur Hasler, *et al.*, "What is Ecology?" in Philip Handler, ed., *Biology and the Future of Man* (Oxford: Oxford University Press, 1970).

18. Frank Fraser Darling, "The Unity of Ecology," Presidential Address delivered at the Aberdeen Meeting of the British Association, August 29, 1963.

19. Paul B. Sears, "Ecology—A Subversive Subject," *BioScience*, vol. 14, no. 7 (1964), 11.

20. Edgar Taschdjian, "The Evolution of Ecological Theory," A.A.A.S. Meeting, December, 1969.

21. Frank Fraser Darling, "A Wider Environment of Ecology and Conservation," *Daedalus* (1967).

22. Paul B. Sears, *Deserts on the March* (Norman: University of Oklahoma Press, 1935).

23. Marston Bates, *The Forest and the Sea* (New York: Random House, Vintage, 1960).

24. Gordon Alexander, *Biology* (New York: Barnes & Noble, 1961).

25. Robert L. Smith, *Ecology and Field Biology* (New York: Harper and Row, 1966).

26. Plato, *The Republic* (Modern Students Library).

27. Will Durant, *The Story of Philosophy* (New York: Simon and Schuster, 1926).

28. Robert L. Heilbroner, *The Worldly Philosophers* (New York: Simon and Schuster, 1953).

29. Frank Fraser Darling and Raymond F. Dasmann, "The Ecosystem View of Human Society," *Impact* (April-June, 1969).

30. Garrett Hardin, "Not Peace, but Ecology," Brookhaven Symposia, no. 22.

31. Edward J. Kormondy, *Readings in Ecology* (Englewood Cliffs, N.J.: Prentice-Hall, 1965).

32. Raymond L. Lindeman, "The Trophic-Dynamic Aspect of Ecology," *Ecology,* vol. 23 (1942), 399–418.

33. Aldo Leopold, *A Sand County Almanac* (Oxford: Oxford University Press, 1953).

34. Robert W. Stock, "Saving the World the Ecologist's Way," *The New York Times Magazine* (October 5, 1969).

35. David M. Gates and Gordon Harrison, "Ecology: The New Great Chain of Being," *Natural History Magazine* (December, 1968).

36. Arthur S. Boughey, *Ecology of Populations* (New York: Macmillan, 1968).

CHAPTER TWO. *The Closed System*

1. Richard D. Lyons, "Lovell Reports Astronauts Felt Death Was Near," *The New York Times* (April 25, 1970).

2. "The Three Astronauts Tell What Happened Aboard the Crippled Apollo 13," *Life* (May 1, 1970).

3. Harold M. Schmeck, Jr., "Homemade System Removes Excess Carbon Dioxide From Spaceship," *The New York Times* (April 16, 1970).

4. *Parametric Study of Manned Life Support Systems*, NASA CR73282 (January, 1969).

5. *The Closed Life-Support System*, NASA SP-134 (1967).

6. Jacob Shapira, *et al.*, "Current Research on Regenerative Systems," *COSPAR Life Sciences and Space Research VII* (May, 1968).

7. Jacob Shapira, "Regenerated Pure Nutrients as Foods for Long Duration Space Missions" (1969).

8. NASA Ames Release 70-3 (February 4, 1970).

9. Odum, *Fundamentals of Ecology*, cited for Chapter One.

10. Stephen A. Forbes, "The Lake as a Microcosm," Bulletin of the Peoria Scientific Association, 1887.

11. Darling, "A Wider Environment of Ecology and Conservation," cited for Chapter One.

12. Elton, *Animal Ecology*, cited for Chapter One.

13. Smith, *Ecology and Field Biology*, cited for Chapter One.

14. Kormondy, *Concepts of Ecology*, cited for Chapter One.

15. Walter Sullivan, "The Sun Shines Less Brightly Than Scientists Once Believed," *The New York Times* (March 26, 1970).

16. William Shakespeare, *Hamlet*.

17. Galen E. Jones, "The Living Economy of the Sea," *Environments of Man* (Cambridge, Mass.: Addison-Wesley, 1968).

18. Gates and Harrison, "Ecology: The New Great Chain of Being," cited for Chapter One.

19. Handler, ed., *Biology and the Future of Man*, cited for Chapter One.

20. Cole, "Can the World Be Saved?" cited for Chapter One.

21. A. Laurence Pringle, "Feeding a Hungry World," *Nature and Science* (April 13, 1970), 7–13.

22. S. Fred Singer, "Environmental Quality—When Does Growth Become Too Expensive?" A.A.A.S. Meeting, December, 1969.

23. LaMont Cole, "The Scope and Extent of the Environmental Crisis," lecture at the American Museum of Natural History, March, 1970.

24. Clair C. Patterson with Joseph D. Salvia, "Lead in the Modern Environment: How Much Is Natural?" *Scientist and Citizen* (April, 1968).

25. "Atmospheric Lead," *Scientist and Citizen* (October, 1968).

26. George M. Woodwell, interview, March, 1969.

27. Charles F. Wurster, Jr., interview, March, 1969.

28. David Siddon, "A Wonderful Bird *Was* the Pelican," *Los Angeles Times Magazine* (July 13, 1969).

CHAPTER THREE. *The Stable System*

1. Frank W. Preston, "Diversity and Stability in the Biological World," Brookhaven Symposia, no. 22 (May, 1969).

2. George B. Schaller, "This Gentle & Elegant Cat," *Natural History Magazine* (June, 1970).

3. "The Biomedical Foundations of Manned Space Flight," a report of the Space and Technology Panel of the President's Science Advisory Committee (November, 1969).

4. William Alanson Bryan, *Natural History of Hawaii* (Honolulu: Hawaiian Gazette Co. Ltd., 1915).

5. "Hawaii Plagued by Rat Problem," *The New York Times* (August 17, 1969).

6. Kormondy, *Concepts of Ecology*, cited for Chapter One.

7. David M. Gates, "Climate and Stability," Brookhaven Symposia, no. 22 (May, 1969).

8. Warren P. Porter and David M. Gates, "Thermodynamic Equilibria of Animals with Environment," *Ecological Monographs*, vol. 39 (Summer, 1969), 245–270.

9. Robert G. Fleagle, "Atmosphere," *Encyclopedia Americana* (1965).

10. Louis J. Battan, interview, National Educational Television, April, 1970.

11. Armand N. Spitz, *Weather* (New York: Bantam, 1967).

12. Charles F. Cooper and William C. Jolly, "Ecological Effects of Weather Modification," University of Michigan, School of Natural Resources (May, 1969).

13. John Brereton quotation in Bil Gilbert, "Wildlife in America," *The Saturday Evening Post* (July, 1967).

14. Sears, *Deserts on the March*, cited for Chapter One.

15. Leopold, *A Sand County Almanac*, cited for Chapter One.

16. Odum, *Fundamentals of Ecology*, cited for Chapter One.

17. Farb, *Ecology*, cited for Chapter One.

18. Henry J. Oosting, "Plant Ecology and Geography," *Encyclopedia Americana* (1965).

19. Frank M. Stead, "Desalting California," *Environment* (June, 1969).

20. W. C. Lowdermilk, "Conquest of the Land Through 7,000 Years," U.S. Department of Agriculture Soil Conservation Service, 1953.

21. Robert Zelnick, "Oil Rush of '70," *The New York Times Magazine* (March 1, 1970).

22. Eugene P. Odum, *Ecology* (New York: Holt, Rinehart and Winston, 1963).

23. Alex Shigo, "The Death and Decay of Trees," *Natural History Magazine* (March, 1969).

24. Desert-tundra-forest comparison based on data from L. E. Rodin and N. I. Bazilevic. *Doklady Akademii Nauk. S.S.S.R.*, 157 (1964), 215–218.

25. John H. Storer, *The Web of Life* (New York: Signet, 1953).

26. Jack Focht, "An Ecosystem Is a Partnership in Nature," *The New York Times* (February 25, 1968).

27. Singer, "Environmental Quality: When Does Growth Become Too Expensive?" cited for Chapter Two.

28. George M. Woodwell, "Effects of Pollution on the Structure and Physiology of Ecosystems," *Science*, Vol. 168 (April 24, 1970), 429–433.

30. Arthur D. Hasler and Bruce Ingersoll, "Dwindling Lakes," *Natural History Magazine* (November, 1968).

31. Eugene P. Odum, "The Strategy of Ecosystem Development," *Science* (April 18, 1969), 164–262.

CHAPTER FOUR. *The Diverse System*

1. "The Starfish Eaters," *Time Magazine* (May 25, 1970).

2. "The Great Barrier Reef," documentary broadcast on NBC Television, May 22, 1970.

3. Hardin, "Not Peace, but Ecology," cited for Chapter One.

4. "Bustards at 12 O'Clock High," *Time Magazine* (January 12, 1970).

5. Kormondy, *Concepts of Ecology*, cited for Chapter One.

6. Boughey, *Ecology of Populations*, cited for Chapter One.

7. Odum, *Fundamentals of Ecology*, cited for Chapter One.

8. Smith, *Ecology and Field Biology*, cited for Chapter One.

9. Edward Abbey, "Let Us Now Praise Mountain Lions," *Life* (March, 1970).

10. Richard G. Van Gelder, "Spacing in Animal Populations," lecture at the American Museum of Natural History, March 25, 1970.

11. Richard G. Van Gelder, "Population Dynamics and the Problem of Overpopulation," lecture at the American Museum of Natural History, April 1, 1970.

12. Justus Liebig, "Organic Chemistry in Its Application to Vegetable Physiology and Agriculture," *Liebig's Complete Works* (Philadelphia: T.B. Peterson, 1841).

13. Nelson G. Hairston, Frederick E. Smith, and Lawrence B. Slobodkin, "Community Structure, Population Control, and Competition," *American Naturalist*, vol. 94 (1960), 421–425.

14. George M. Woodwell, "Radiation and the Patterns of Nature," *Science*, vol. 156 (April 28, 1967), 461–470.

15. Farb, *Ecology*, cited for Chapter One.

16. Elton, *Animal Ecology*, cited for Chapter One.

17. Darling, "A Wider Environment of Ecology and Conservation," cited for Chapter One.

18. Paul S. Martin, "Wanted: A Suitable Herbivore," *Natural History Magazine* (February, 1969).

19. *The Christian Science Monitor* (March 24, 1970).

20. Stock, "Saving the World the Ecologist's Way," cited for Chapter One.

21. Stewart L. Udall, *The Quiet Crisis* (New York: Holt, Rinehart and Winston, 1963).

22. George Laycock, "The Last Parakeet," *Audubon Magazine* (March, 1969).

23. Konrad Z. Lorenz, *King Solomon's Ring* (New York: Crowell, 1952).

24. Jane E. Brody, "Sickle Cell Anemia Yielding Its Secrets," *The New York Times* (March 15, 1970).

25. René J. Dubos, *Mirage of Health* (New York: Harper, 1959).

26. Bil Gilbert, *How Animals Communicate* (New York: Pantheon, 1966).

27. *Time Magazine* (June 8, 1970).

28. Edward T. Hall, *The Hidden Dimension* (New York: Anchor, 1969).

29. Odum, "The Strategy of Ecosystem Development," cited for Chapter Three.

30. Handler, *Biology and the Future of Man*, cited for Chapter One.

31. John J. Christian, "Social Subordination, Population Density, and Mammalian Evolution," *Science* (April 3, 1970).

32. Charles Elton, *The Ecology of Invasions by Animals and Plants* (London: Methuen; New York: Barnes and Noble, 1958).

33. Robert Erb, interview at The Franklin Institute, November, 1969.

34. *The New York Times*, March 22, 1970.

35. P. B. S. Lissaman and Carl A. Shollenberger, "Formation Flight of Birds," *Science* (May 22, 1970).

CHAPTER FIVE. *Epilogue and Prologue*

1. Bates, *The Forest and the Sea*, cited for Chapter One.
2. Arnold M. Schultz, "A Study of an Ecosystem: The Arctic Tundra," *The Ecosystem Concept in Natural Resource Management* (New York: Academic Press, 1969).
3. René J. Dubos, *So Human an Animal* (New York: Scribners, 1968).
4. Barry Commoner, *Science and Survival* (New York: Viking Compass, 1963).
5. Theodore H. White, "How Do We Get From Here to There?" *Life* (June 26, 1970).
6. James M. Naughton, "Nixon Proposes Two New Agencies on Environment," *The New York Times* (July 10, 1970).

CHAPTER SIX. Ecce Homo: *Behold the Man*

1. Walter Sullivan, "Astronomers Detect a Substance That May Have Aided Evolution," *The New York Times* (June 17, 1970).
2. George Gaylord Simpson, "The First Three Billion Years of Community Evolution," Brookhaven Symposium, May, 1969.
3. LaMont C. Cole, "Man's Ecosystem," *BioScience* (April, 1966).
4. Boughey, *Ecology of Populations*, cited for Chapter One.
5. Charles F. Hockett and Robert Acher, "The Human Revolution," *Current Anthropology*, vol. 5, no. 3 (1964), 135.
6. Sherwood L. Washburn, "Tools and Human Evolution," *Scientific American* (September, 1960).
7. Charles F. Hockett, "The Origin of Speech," *Scientific American* (September, 1960).
8. Marshal D. Sahlins, "The Origin of Society," *Scientific American* (September, 1960).
9. Walter Sullivan, "Scientist Urges Rearing Lost Species' Relatives," *The New York Times* (March 17, 1970).
10. Walter Sullivan, "How Man Became a Mass Killer 11,000 Years Ago," *The New York Times* (March 22, 1970).

11. Nancy Hicks, "Leopard Studied in Role as Predator," *The New York Times* (March 22, 1970).

12. Martin, "Wanted: A Suitable Herbivore," cited for Chapter Four.

13. Van Gelder, "Spacing in Animal Populations," cited for Chapter Four.

14. Lawrence F. Hinkle, Jr., "Modern Environments and Their Influence on Human Health," lecture, April 8, 1970.

15. Edward S. Deevey, Jr., "The Human Population," *Scientific American* (September, 1960).

16. Lorenz, *King Solomon's Ring*, cited for Chapter Four.

17. Darling, "The Unity of Ecology," cited for Chapter One.

18. Robert J. Braidwood, "The Agricultural Revolution," *Scientific American* (September, 1960).

19. Robert M. Adams, "The Origin of Cities," *Scientific American* (September, 1960).

20. Darling and Dasmann, "The Ecosystem View of Human Society," cited for Chapter One.

21. Udall, *The Quiet Crisis*, cited for Chapter Four.

22. Frank Fraser Darling, "Wilderness and Plenty," The Reith Lectures, *The Listener* (November 20, 1969).

23. Fairfield Osborn, *Our Plundered Planet* (Boston: Little, Brown, 1948).

24. Frederick Sargent, II, and Demitri B. Shimkin, "Biology, Society, and Culture in Human Ecology," *BioScience* (August, 1965).

25. Marston Bates, "The Human Ecosystem," *Resources and Man* (San Francisco: Freeman, 1969).

26. Lynn White, Jr., "The Historical Roots of Our Ecological Crisis," *Science*, vol. 155 (1967), 1203–1207.

27. Jacob Burckhardt, *The Civilization of the Renaissance in Italy* [Phaidon Press, (orig.) 1860].

28. *The New York Times* (June 7, 1970).

29. M. King Hubbert, "Energy Resources," *Resources and Man* (San Francisco: Freeman, 1969).

30. Michael Evenari, "Ecological Farming," *Impact* (April-June, 1969).

31. Kenneth E. Boulding, "Economics and Ecology," *Future Environments for North America* (Natural History Press, 1966).

32. Heilbroner, *The Worldly Philosophers*, cited for Chapter One.

33. Edgar Taschdjian, "The Evolution of Ecological Theory," A.A.A.S. Meeting, December, 1969.

34. Sanford Rose, "The Economics of Environmental Quality," *Fortune* (February, 1970).

35. Smith, *Ecology and Field Biology*, cited for Chapter One.

36. Hardin, "Not Peace, but Ecology," cited for Chapter One.

37. Allan T. Demaree, "Cars and Cities on a Collision Course," *Fortune* (February, 1970).

38. Garrett Hardin, "The Tragedy of the Commons," *Science*, vol. 162 (December 13, 1968).

39. Richard A. Falk, address to Natural Resources Defense Council Conference, Princeton, N.J., March 21, 1970.

40. Stock, "Saving the World the Ecologist's Way," cited for Chapter One.

41. Prince Philip, Duke of Edinburgh, "Man's Wildlife Heritage Faces Extinction," *National Geographic* (November, 1962).

42. "Vanishing Wildlife," *Time* (June 8, 1970).

43. Roger Revelle, "Future Changes in Man's Earthly Environment," Symposium on Man-Made Changes in the Environment, Royal Society, London, September, 1969.

44. Jack Pearce, interview, November, 1969.

45. *Proceedings of Symposium on Human Ecology*, U.S. Department of Health, Education and Welfare (November, 1968).

46. Pierre Dansereau, "Ecological Impact and Human Ecology," *Future Environments of North America* (Natural History Press, 1966).

47. Frederick Sargent, II, communication, May 18, 1970.

48. Lynton K. Caldwell, "Centers of Excellence for the Study of Human Ecology," H.E.W. symposium (November, 1968).

49. Robert H. Whittaker, "Evolution of Diversity in Plant Communities," Brookhaven symposium (May, 1969).

50. "Model Man," *Time* (May, 1970).

51. George M. Woodwell, interview, October 7, 1969.

CHAPTER SEVEN. *Civilization's Summit*

1. Darling and Dasmann, "The Ecosystem View of Human Society," cited for Chapter One.

2. Jerome Kretchmer, statement, April 9, 1970.

3. Smith, *Ecology and Field Biology*, cited for Chapter One.

4. Herbert Butterfield, "The Scientific Revolution," *Scientific American* (September, 1960).

5. "Ecology of a Ghetto," *Time* (April 6, 1970).

6. *The New York Times* (February 19, 1970).

7. Odum, *Fundamentals of Ecology*, cited for Chapter One.

8. F. F. Darling and John P. Milton, eds., *Future Environments of North America* (Natural History Press, 1966).

9. Constantine A. Doxiadis, "Ecumenopolis, World City of Tomorrow," *Impact* (April-June, 1969).

10. Edwin H. Marston, interview, June 10, 1970.

11. Edwin H. Marston, letter, *The Village Voice* (February 5, 1970).

12. Demaree, "Cars and Cities on a Collision Course," cited for Chapter Six.

13. William Vogt, "Population Patterns and Movements," *Future Environments of North America* (Natural History Press, 1966).

14. Odum, *Ecology*, cited for Chapter Three.

15. E. S. Savas, "Cybernetics in City Hall," *Science*, vol. 168 (May 29, 1970).

16. Jay W. Forrester, "Overlooked Reasons for Our Social Troubles," *Fortune* (December, 1969).

17. William K. Stevens, "Computer Used as Guide to Expert Seeking Way Out of Labyrinth of Urban Problems," *The New York Times* (October 3, 1969).

18. Jay W. Forrester, *Urban Dynamics* (Cambridge, Mass.: M.I.T. Press, 1969).

19. "The Great New Chain of Being," *Natural History*, cited for Chapter One.

20. Crawford S. Holling, "Stability in Ecological and Social Systems," Brookhaven Symposium.

21. *Time* (October 10, 1969).

22. *Life* (October, 1969).

23. Ian McHarg, "What Would You Do With, Say, Staten Island?" *Natural History* (April, 1969).

24. Ian McHarg, *Design With Nature* (Natural History Press, 1969).

25. John B. Calhoun, "Population Density and Social Pathology," *Scientific American* (February, 1962).

26. Daniel H. Carson, "Population Concentration and Human Stress," Byron P. Rourke, ed., in *Explorations in the Psychology of Stress and Anxiety* (Longmans Canada Limited, 1969).

27. René J. Dubos, "The Human Environment in Technological Societies," *The Rockefeller University Review* (July-August, 1968).

28. Caroline Bird, "What New York Can Learn from the World's Largest City," *New York Magazine* (February, 1970).

29. George M. Woodwell, "The Biosphere Packing Problem," *Ecology* (Winter, 1970).

30. Max Ways, "How to Think About the Environment," *Fortune* (February, 1970).

31. René J. Dubos, interview, September, 1969.

CHAPTER EIGHT. *Symptoms*

1. Dubos, *Mirage of Health*, cited for Chapter Four.

2. R. Llewellyn, *How Green Was My Valley*.

3. Lee A. DuBridge, address to the 13th National Conference of the U.S. National Commission for UNESCO, November 23, 1969.

4. Cole, "The Scope and Extent of the Environmental Crisis," cited for Chapter Two.

5. H. G. Wells, *World Set Free* (1913).

6. Singer, "Environmental Quality: When Does Growth Become Too Expensive?" cited for Chapter Two.

7. Elmer Robinson and Robert C. Robbins, "Sources, Abundance, and Fate of Gaseous Atmospheric Pollutants," Stanford Research Institute, February, 1968.

8. Sandra Blakeslee, "Pollution Study Finds Nature More Efficient Housekeeper Than Man," *The New York Times* (February 5, 1969).

9. Kormondy, *Concepts of Ecology*, cited for Chapter One.

10. Harold P. Koenig, interview, October, 1969.

11. Rudy Garcia, "40 of 435 Hit by Lead Poison," *New York Daily News* (June 20, 1970).

12. Bayard Webster, "Extremism Scored in Birth Debate," *The New York Times* (November 2, 1969).

13. *The New York Times* (December 15, 1969).

14. Walter Sullivan, "How Not to Curb Pollution," *The New York Times* (December 21, 1969).

15. *Eutrophication,* Proceedings of a symposium, National Academy of Sciences, 1969.

16. *Sea Secrets,* vol. I, no. 1 (February, 1970).

17. Paul A. Erickson and John T. Reynolds, "The Ecology of a Reservoir," *Natural History* (November, 1969).

18. Hardin, "Not Peace, but Ecology," cited for Chapter One.

19. Harold M. Schmeck, "Warning Sounded on a Sulphur Gas," *The New York Times* (May 20, 1970).

20. Dean E. Abrahamson, "Environmental Cost of Electric Power," Scientists' Institute for Public Information, 1970.

21. Sidney J. Socolar and Edward L. Friedman, "Health and Safety Aspects of Nuclear Power," N.Y. Scientists' Committee for Public Information, March 4, 1970.

22. Robert M. Smith, "A.E.C. Scored on Storing Waste," *The New York Times* (March 7, 1970).

23. M. King Hubbert, "Energy Resources," *Resources and Man* (San Francisco: Freeman, 1969).

24. Odum, *Fundamentals of Ecology*, cited for Chapter One.

25. D. G. Jacobs, *Sources of Tritium and Its Behavior Upon Release to the Environment* (A.E.C., 1968).

26. John W. Gofman and Arthur R. Tamplin, "Radiation: The Invisible Casualties," *Environment* (April, 1970).

27. Arthur Tamplin, "Man-Made Radiation in the Biosphere," A.A.A.S. Meeting, December 28, 1969.

28. Eric Pace, "Control of Radioactive Wastes in Sea Urged at Experts' Parley," *The New York Times* (July 1, 1970).

29. Joel W. Hedgpeth, "The Oceans: World Sump," *Environment* (April, 1970).

30. Woodwell, "Effects of Pollution on the Structure and Physiology of Ecosystems," cited for Chapter Three.

CHAPTER NINE. *The Ruptured Chain*

1. Raul Cardenas, lecture, February, 1970.
2. Lawrence Wright, *Clean and Decent* (New York: Viking, 1960).
3. Maurice M. Feldman, report, April 9, 1970.
4. Martin Waldron, "Millions Are Spent to Fight Pollution of Ocean Beaches," *The New York Times* (June 29, 1970).
5. Singer, "Environmental Quality: When Does Growth Become Too Expensive?" cited for Chapter Two.
6. "The Age of Effluence," *Time Magazine*, (May 10, 1968).
7. Neal Stanford, "Sounding the Alarm on Pollution Threat," *The Christian Science Monitor* (February 27, 1970).
8. David Bird, "Problem of Ridding City of Garbage Eludes a Solution," *The New York Times* (March 24, 1970).
9. "New York City Environmental Prospectus—1970."
10. Athelstan Spilhaus, "The Next Industrial Revolution," *Science*, vol. 167, no. 3926 (March 27, 1970).
11. Griswold L. Moeller, press briefing, April 9, 1970.
12. Samuel J. Kearing, Jr., "The Politics of Garbage," *New York Magazine*, 1970.
13. Neil L. Clemons, "Yesterday's Newspaper Finds a New Use: It's 'Laundered,' Made Into Today's Paper," *The Wall Street Journal* (January 5, 1970).
14. C. H. Waddington, "Final Paper With a Look Into the Future," Symposium on Man-Made Changes in the Environment, September 30, 1969.
15. Gerald Lauer—Interview at N.Y.U. Institute of Environmental Medicine, February 26, 1970.
16. "G.M. Rolls Scrap Into Usable Steel," *The New York Times* (February 28, 1970).
17. "Nixon Aide Assails No-Return Bottles As a Litter Hazard," *The New York Times* (March 25, 1970).
18. Plan to Buy Back Used Bottles Set," *The New York Times* (July 1, 1970).
19. S. F. Hulbert, *et al.*, "Improving Packaging Disposability," First National Conference on Packaging Wastes, September 24, 1969.
20. "A Plastic for Ecologists," *Time* (May 11, 1970).

CHAPTER TEN. *By Their Fruits You Shall Know Them*

1. *The New York Times* (March 8, 1937).
2. "Grasslands II: Broken Sod," *Fortune* (November, 1935).
3. "Grasslands III: Dust," *Fortune* (November, 1935).
4. Bates, *The Forest and the Sea*, cited for Chapter One.
5. Smith, *Ecology and Field Biology*, cited for Chapter One.
6. Sears, *Deserts on the March*, cited for Chapter One.
7. Odum, *Fundamentals of Ecology*, cited for Chapter One.
8. Odum, *Ecology*, cited for Chapter Three.
9. Cooper and Jolly, "Ecological Effects of Weather Modification," cited for Chapter Three.
10. Taschdjian, "The Evolution of Ecological Theory," cited for Chapter One.
11. "Too High a Farm Ceiling," *The New York Times* (August 18, 1970).
12. Edward Higbee, *Farms and Farmers in an Urban Age* (New York: The Twentieth Century Fund, 1963).
13. William Robbins, "Farm Policy Helps Make Rural Rich Richer," *The New York Times* (April 5, 1970).
14. "Hard Times in the Country," documentary broadcast by National Educational Television, May, 1970.
15. Jules B. Billard, "The Revolution in American Agriculture," *National Geographic* (February, 1970).
16. Evenari, "Ecological Farming," cited for Chapter Six.
17. Morton W. Miller and George G. Berg, eds., *Chemical Fallout* (Springfield, Ill.: Charles C Thomas, 1969).
18. Richard Lehnert, "Ecologists Analyze Pollution: Modern Agricultural Production Short-Circuits Nature's Cycles," *Michigan Farmer* (November 14, 1970).
19. Clifton R. Wharton, Jr., "The Green Revolution: Cornucopia or Pandora's Box?" *Foreign Affairs* (April, 1969).
20. "The Rattle in the Rice Bowl," *The Economist* (April 4, 1970).
21. "India: The Land-Grab War," *Newsweek* (August 3, 1970).
22. Stead, "Desalting California," cited for Chapter Three.
23. "Quenching California's Thirst," *Time Magazine* (July 6, 1970).

24. Kimmis Hendrick, "California Water Plan Stirs Protest," *The Christian Science Monitor* (April 4, 1970).

25. Abrahamson, "Environmental Cost of Electric Power," cited for Chapter Eight.

26. Dana Adams Schmidt, "Aswan Dam Alters Marine Ecology," *The New York Times* (June 7, 1970).

27. Karl F. Lagler, ed., *Man-Made Lakes* (New York: U.N. Food and Agriculture Organization, 1969).

28. Singer, "Environmental Quality: When Does Growth Become Too Expensive?" cited for Chapter Two.

29. John Allen May, "Britain Adopts Codes for 'Factory Farming,'" *The Christian Science Monitor* (October 23, 1969).

30. David Bird, "Experts Debate Farm Pollution," *The New York Times* (January 25, 1970).

31. Barry Commoner, "Nature Unbalanced," *Scientist and Citizen* (January-February, 1968).

32. George W. Irving, Jr., "Agricultural Pest Control and the Environment," *Science* (June 19, 1970).

33. C. E. Yarwood, "Man-Made Plant Diseases," *Science* (April 10, 1970).

34. Richard L. Doutt and Ray F. Smith, "The Pesticide Syndrome—Diagnosis and Suggested Prophylaxis," A.A.A.S. Meeting, December 30, 1969.

35. "Report to Executives: What's Coming in Chemicals," *Business Week* (November 25, 1944).

36. "DDT Marches On," *American Journal of Public Health* (April, 1951).

37. Charles F. Wurster, Jr., interviews, March, April, October, 1969.

38. George M. Woodwell, interviews, March, April, October, 1969.

39. Gordon Conway, "DDT on Balance," *Environment* (September, 1969).

40. "Diminishing Returns," *Environment* (September, 1969).

41. Charles F. Wurster, Jr., "Chlorinated Hydrocarbon Insecticides and Avian Reproduction: How Are They Related?" *Chemical Fallout* (1969).

42. Hedgpeth, "The Oceans: World Sump," cited for Chapter Eight.

43. Kevin P. Shea, "Unwanted Harvest," *Environment* (September, 1969).

44. Reo Duggan, interview, March, 1969.

45. Charles F. Wurster, Jr., "DDT Reduces Photosynthesis by Marine Phytoplankton," *Science* (March 29, 1968).

46. James W. Moorman, Charles R. Halpern, and Edward Berlin, "Petition to U.S. Department of Agriculture Requesting the Suspension and Cancellation of Registration of Economic Poisons Containing DDT" (October 31, 1969).

47. Food and Drug Administration Release 69-23, April 4, 1969.

48. "Ban on DDT Sales Voted in Michigan," *The New York Times* (April 17, 1969).

49. Richard D. Lyons, "Partial DDT Ban Starts in 30 Days, Virtual Halt by '71," *The New York Times* (November 21, 1969).

50. Hairston, Smith, and Slobodkin, "Community Structure, Population Control, and Competition," cited for Chapter Four.

51. Woodwell, "Effects of Pollution on the Structure and Physiology of Ecosystems," cited for Chapter Three.

52. A. Dexter Hinckley, "Alternatives to DDT," unpublished paper.

53. Robert van den Bosch, "Pesticides: Prescribing for the Ecosystem," *Environment* (April, 1970).

54. Paul DeBach, "Some Ecological Aspects of Insect Eradication," *Bulletin of the Entomological Society of America* (December, 1964).

55. Carl B. Huffaker, "The Theory and Practice of Biological Control," A.A.A.S. Meeting, December 30, 1969.

56. Robert L. Rudd, *Pesticides and the Living Landscape* (Madison: U. of Wisconsin Press, 1966).

57. Paul DeBach, David Rosen, and C. E. Kennett, "Biological Control of Coccids by Introduced Natural Enemies," A.A.A.S. Meeting, December 29-30, 1969.

58. Robert van den Bosch, *et al.*, "The Developing Program of Integrated Control of Cotten Pests in California," A.A.A.S. Meeting, December 31, 1969.

CHAPTER ELEVEN. *Will Success Spoil* Homo Sapiens?

1. Thomas Malthus, "An Essay on the Principle of Population," 1798.

2. "Effects of Population Growth on Natural Resources and the Environment," Hearings before a Subcommittee of the Committee on Government Operations, House of Representatives, September 15–16, 1969.

3. Jean Mayer, "Toward a Non-Malthusian Population Policy," *Columbia Forum* (Summer, 1969).

4. Sandra Blakeslee, "High-Protein Food, Created in Laboratories, Is Starting To Enter the Consumer's Diet," *The New York Times* (March 1, 1970).

5. Lester R. Brown, A.A.A.S. Meeting, reported in *The New York Times* (December 30, 1969).

6. John D. Chapman, "Interactions Between Man and His Resources," *Resources and Man* (San Francisco: Freeman, 1969).

7. Hans H. Landsberg, "The U.S. Resource Outlook: Quantity and Quality," *Daedalus* (Fall, 1967).

8. Kormondy, *Concepts of Ecology*, cited for Chapter One.

9. Lincoln H. Day, "The Population in the United States," *The 99th Hour* (Chapel Hill: U. of North Carolina, 1967).

10. Judith Blake Davis, "Population Policy for Americans: Is the Government Being Misled?" *Science* (May 2, 1969).

11. Hinkle, "Modern Environments and Their Influence on Human Health," cited for Chapter Six.

12. Bates, "The Human Ecosystem," cited for Chapter Six.

13. Bates, *The Forest and the Sea*, cited for Chapter One.

14. Boughey, *Ecology of Populations*, cited for Chapter One.

15. Richard M. Nixon, "Problems of Population Growth," July 18, 1969.

16. Paul R. Ehrlich, *The Population Bomb* (New York: Ballantine Books, 1969).

17. Robert C. Cook and Jane Lecht, *People! An Introduction to the Study of Population* (Washington, D.C.: Population Reference Bureau, 1968).

18. Van Gelder, "Population Dynamics and the Problem of Overpopulation," cited for Chapter Four.

19. Edwin L. Dale, Jr., "A Nixon Adviser Doubts Overpopulation," *The New York Times* (March 29, 1970).

20. Woodwell, interviews, cited for Chapter Ten.

21. Holling, "Stability in Ecological and Social Systems," cited for Chapter Seven.

22. Harold M. Schmeck, Jr., "Scientist Finds Ecology Excesses," *The New York Times* (May 5, 1970).

23. Symposium, "Is There an Optimum Level of Population?" A.A.A.S. Meeting, December, 1969.

24. Preston Cloud, Jr., "Resources, Population, and Quality of Life," A.A.A.S. Meeting, December, 1969.

25. Walter Sullivan, "Doctor Says U.S. Has Passed Optimum Population," *The New York Times*, (December 30, 1969).

26. Singer, "Environmental Quality: When Does Growth Become Too Expensive?" cited for Chapter Two.

27. H. Bentley Glass, "Is There an Optimal Size of Population: Genetic Considerations," A.A.A.S. Meeting, December, 1969.

28. Odum, *Fundamentals of Ecology*, cited for Chapter One.

29. M. King Hubbert, "Energy Resources," *Resources and Man* (San Francisco: Freeman, 1969).

30. Abrahamson, "Environmental Cost of Electric Power," cited for Chapter Eight.

31. N.A.S. Committee on Resources and Man (San Francisco: Freeman, 1969).

32. Thomas S. Lovering, "Mineral Resources from the Land," *Resources and Man* (San Francisco: Freeman, 1969).

33. Roy Reed, "Dangerous Levels of Mercury Found in Lakes and Streams in 14 Eastern States by U.S. Investigators," *The New York Times* (July 9, 1970).

CHAPTER TWELVE. *Perspective*

1. N.A.S. Committee, *Resources and Man*, cited for Chapter Eleven.

2. Woodwell, interview, cited for Chapter Ten.

3. Stock, "Saving the World the Ecologist's Way," cited for Chapter One.

4. "The Advent of Big Biology," *Time Magazine* (February, 1970).

Index

Index